Jake Svenson had no right to be so contemptuous of her, fumed Claire to herself, when it was quite obvious what his relationship with the beautiful actress Marianne Lejeune was!

WRECKER'S BRIDE

BY

KATHRYN CRANMER

MILLS & BOON LIMITED
15–16 BROOK'S MEWS
LONDON W1A 1DR

*First published in Great Britain 1985
by Mills & Boon Limited*

© Kathryn Cranmer 1985

*Australian copyright 1985
Philippine copyright 1985
This edition 1985*

ISBN 0 263 74987 8

*Set in Monophoto Times 10 on 10 pt.
01–0385 · 62724*

*Made and printed in Great Britain by
Richard Clay (The Chaucer Press) Ltd,
Bungay, Suffolk*

CHAPTER ONE

'FOR God's sake, Claire, don't be so damned stuffy!' Alan began to pace the floor angrily as though the action might help to dissipate some of the nervous tension he was clearly feeling, but if that was his purpose it was obviously not having the desired effect and he stopped suddenly, shooting an angry glance at the tall, slim girl standing by the window. 'It's not as though we were strangers. Good Lord, we've practically lived in each other's pockets for the last few months!' He paused and tried a new tack. 'You say you're both broke?'

The girl shrugged her shoulders, the glance she threw in his direction holding a bewildering mixture of emotions. 'You know we are,' she remarked in faintly husky tones, turning her head slightly so that the early spring sunshine caught the loose tendrils of her auburn hair, changing them to burnished bronze.

'You definitely need someone else to share the flat with you,' Alan persisted.

'You know that too,' she replied steadily. She looked calm but in fact she was holding her own volatile temper on a tight rein. She was becoming increasingly tired of Alan's persistence, but he obviously saw nothing of her inward turmoil. He put one hand to his forehead and raked it through his thick lion's mane of hair.

'Hell, how can I get through to you? You're so damned cool about the whole thing. You're driving me wild. What can I say to convince you?' He resumed his angry pacing and Claire watched him from shadowed eyes. Their arguments were becoming more frequent and more heated and the subject under discussion always seemed to be the same.

Alan stopped in front of her, his face still set in angry lines although he was clearly making an immense effort to control his voice, his tones measured and reasonable: 'You need another flatmate. I'm in love with you. I can't see any possible objection to my moving in.'

He was speaking to her as though she was a recalcitrant child, Claire realised. He wanted to make her angry, she was aware of that. It increased her vulnerability, but today she had no intention of letting him get under her skin in that way.

'I've told you before that I don't happen to think I am being stuffy,' she said, removing her gaze from his angry face and turning to stare out of the window, not really seeing the small gardens still struggling to throw off their bedraggled winter plumage, her thoughts instead on Alan Crosby and the ultimatum he had just delivered. She knew that he considered marriage an outdated institution and appeared to be totally unable to understand her reluctance to become his mistress. Maybe she was old-fashioned, but she wanted to be very sure of her own feelings before she committed herself completely to any man.

Her eyes flickered towards him again, studying him with an objectivity that she would not have thought possible a few weeks ago. He was an attractive man and they had a lot of interests in common but their frequent arguments had chipped away at the foundations of their relationship and she no longer saw him through quite such rose-tinted spectacles.

'Sometimes I wonder if you can really be true,' Alan said now, his harsh voice interrupting her musings, his stocky, muscular body planted close to hers as he gripped her shoulders and gave them a tiny shake. 'You look real and my God, you certainly feel real, but sometimes I ask myself if there can be anything inside that beautiful exterior except ice.' He turned away, his stance conveying the fierce irritation he was feeling. 'You're very ready to talk about your feelings but when it comes to doing anything about it you're not so damned eager. You look as though you're made of fire, Claire, but I'm beginning to think it must be pack ice all the way through.'

He paused, staring into her eyes as though they would give him a clue to her thoughts, then: 'Don't you care for me at all?' he asked angrily. 'Has it all been pretence?'

'No!' Claire protested. 'You know that's not true. I'm very fond of you, Alan.' His smile was not a pleasant one and Claire would not have cared to repeat the oath which he uttered. Indeed Claire regretted the words the moment she'd said them. She knew that Alan wanted her to say that she was crazy about him, but it was impossible. She just wouldn't mean it. In fact she'd realised while he'd been talking that she had never been as wildly in love with him as she had once thought. It had been an infatuation—and it was over. But looking at his face now she knew she couldn't tell him the truth, not today. Instead she raised her hands in an instinctive gesture of appeal.

'Alan, we've been over all this before . . .'

'Like hell we have!' Without warning he reached forward, his fingers digging painfully into the soft flesh of her shoulders. 'I'm crazy about you, Claire, but I won't wait for ever. This is what I want,' he muttered roughly, drawing her resisting body towards his own, his mouth covering hers, moving hungrily over her soft lips without any show of tenderness.

'Don't do that!' Claire tore herself out of his arms and rubbed the back of one slim hand across her mouth, her own anger rising to meet his, her voice shaking with reaction after the unexpected violence of his kiss. She'd been trying to let him down lightly but clearly he didn't give a damn about her feelings. 'Don't ever do that again,' she said on a trembling breath. 'I'm beginning to think that we've both made a mistake. You don't seem willing to attempt to understand my point of view.'

'And you sure as hell don't attempt to understand mine,' Alan snarled angrily.

Claire's eyes were stormy. 'All you seem to be interested in these days is sex. I'm beginning to think that's all you ever wanted from me.'

'Oh my God! You frigid little . . .' He closed his lips on the final word and shook his head as though he couldn't believe what he was hearing. 'We've been going together for months and I've got absolutely nowhere. Do you think that if sex was the only criterion I would still be hanging around? I would be long gone, believe me. But I'm wasting my breath, aren't I?' he asked in a voice raw with emotion. He picked up his jacket from the back of a chair and thrust his arms into the sleeves with unnecessary violence.

'Grow up, Claire! You're living in the past! Your ideas went out of fashion twenty years ago. You'd better come down to earth quickly before you find that life has passed you by completely. You will be old and grey before you know it and you will never have lived.' He paused, his hand on the half-opened door. 'Give me a ring when you're tired of living in this ivory tower of yours. I'll be more than happy to help you rejoin the human race.'

Claire winced as the outer door slammed to behind him, her sigh of relief tinged with a faint regret as she stood for a moment at the window and watched his stocky figure receding down the street. She had known for some time that their relationship would have to end but still, his departure would leave a gap in her life, they had been friends for a long time; she would miss him. Claire could feel depression settling in and with an impatient sigh she dropped the curtain and moved over to the rather battered stereo unit in one corner of the room.

She knew it was useless to brood. For a brief time she had imagined herself in love with Alan, but now it was finished. With a sigh she dropped to her heels in front of the record rack, her eyes flicking quickly along the album covers. She and her flatmate, Lynn, had quite a wide selection of records and soon a cheerful disco number was thudding out of the speakers and Claire was on her feet, her body moving sinuously to the throbbing rhythm. In fact she was so totally absorbed in the music that she failed to hear the outer door open and close again and it wasn't until the record had finished that she turned her head and saw Lynn standing just inside the door watching her, an expression of fond amusement on her beautiful face.

'Don't tell me, Claire, let me guess. You've been offered a leading role in the comedy you auditioned for this morning.' Lynn smiled and walked forward as she spoke, stripping off her blue quilted jacket and dropping it carelessly on the back of a chair. 'Incidentally it's freezing out there.' She shivered and dropped to her haunches, turning up the pressure on the gas fire before lowering her weight into the nearest armchair. She shot Claire a sideways glance. 'Seriously my love, did you get the part today or are we still both on the bread line?'

Claire shrugged faintly and moving forward sank gracefully to her knees on the hearth rug. Her row with Alan had temporarily erased her other worries but now they came rushing back with a vengeance.

'Yes and yes actually,' she replied with a rueful grimace.

'Explain!' Lynn commanded. 'The pay can't be so bad surely?'

'Much worse than for *Twelfth Night* actually.' That had been her last play with a small, provincial theatre and it had finished ten days ago. 'I'm afraid we're still broke, Lynn. I turned the part down,' she confessed apologetically. 'I'm probably going to kick myself later but the money was so poor and the part so small, not to mention the fact that it involved all the hassle of a touring company.' She paused. 'And then there's the audition for *Wrecker's Bride* coming up shortly. Maybe I'm being over-optimistic but if I could get even a small part in that film the money would be so much better.'

If Lynn was disappointed she didn't show it. 'Don't

look so worried, darling. I'm sure you made the right decision. The only question now is how are we going to eat for the rest of the week?'

'Well I did go and collect my unemployment benefit this morning.'

Lynn pulled a face. 'That's better than nothing I suppose and at least you've earned some money during the last three weeks which is more than I can say. I've only been offered two modelling jobs in the last two months. It was a stupid idea of mine giving up a steady secretarial post for this uncertain profession.'

'Three months is no time at all to become established and you know it,' Claire sighed. She couldn't help feeling guilty. Lynn was blaming herself for their difficulties and yet she had had two opportunities to improve their finances today and turned them both down. 'Alan was here earlier,' she admitted now with faint reluctance. 'He was angling to share the flat again.'

'And he wasn't intending to sleep in the spare room, I take it?' Lynn remarked with an old-fashioned look.

Claire groaned. 'How right you are, but I'm beginning to wonder whether I ought to have taken him up on the offer.' She turned to her friend. 'We had a flaming row as a matter of fact but if I told him I had had second thoughts I think he would still come.'

Lynn was faintly shocked. 'Don't sacrifice yourself for me, darling. He was never my favourite human being, you know that, and I suspect that once he had moved in he would cling to you like glue.' She shot her friend a shrewd glance. 'And if you're still thinking that you could somehow fob him off with a room of his own, don't you believe it. Quite frankly I'm surprised that you've managed to keep him at arm's length for so long. He was obviously nuts about you.' Lynn pulled a face. 'His one redeeming feature in my eyes.'

'I suppose you're right,' Claire sighed, but in spite of everything that had happened she had been fond of Alan, she hadn't wanted to hurt him. 'We did have fun together,' she murmured regretfully. 'And he could be very kind and thoughtful.' She raised her eyes. 'Maybe I wasn't always as responsive as I ought to have been.'

'Rubbish!' Lynn countered instantly. 'He wouldn't have stayed around as long as he did if that was the case.' She saw that Claire was still looking unhappy and pushed herself to her feet, deliberately changing the subject. 'Now, how about some coffee? I could do with something to warm me up. Come into the kitchen and talk to me while I put the kettle on.'

Claire followed Lynn obediently, levering herself on to one of the soft-topped buffets beside the work surface. The flat was small, consisting of two bedrooms, a lounge, the tiny kitchen and an even smaller bathroom. It was situated in an unfashionable area of London and it was shabby but even so the rent absorbed a large part of their earnings—when they had any. Still it was home, and had been since Claire's mother had re-married and gone to live in the States. Claire liked her stepfather but had never been tempted to accompany them. She was determined to continue with her course at drama school and although her mother had tried to persuade her to change her mind, she had eventually accepted Claire's decision with a good grace.

It had been through her new stepfather that Claire had met Lynn. He was an old friend of Lynn's parents and when they heard that Claire was looking for a flat they had suggested that she and Lynn join forces. Claire had been reluctant at first, but now she wouldn't change. Her eyes dwelled affectionately on Lynn's cool blonde beauty. She was a good friend and they had had some marvellous times since moving into the flat together. She would hate to have to move to somewhere cheaper.

Lynn turned to her now, pausing in the act of spooning coffee into two scarlet mugs. 'Don't look so worried, Claire, and stop blaming yourself. I'm sure you made the correct decision today. It would have been stupid to take such a poorly paid job, even without the prospect of the film audition on the horizon. You're surely past the stage of taking work simply for the experience.'

'But not past the stage of taking work simply to eat,' Claire responded gloomily.

Lynn pulled a face, handing Claire a brimming mug of coffee. 'Don't be an idiot, love.' Lynn pulled out a buffet and hoisted herself on to it, facing Claire with a deliberately cheerful smile. 'Stop fretting,' she urged. 'Drink your coffee and tell me about the audition. It's on Friday didn't you say?'

'Hmm, at ten o'clock.' Claire sipped her coffee slowly before adding: 'I'm nervous as usual, but at least it's not long to wait and worry and Mike has promised me a lift so I should get there without too much trouble.'

Mike's wife, Joan, was one of Claire's oldest friends. They had gone through school together and kept in touch after Claire had left to attend drama school. Mike had been at the flat one evening when Joan walked in and within two months they had been married. Claire wasn't inclined to believe in love at first sight, but she had to admit it had worked that way for them.

Lynn was still talking about the audition and Claire forced herself to concentrate. 'Will there be much competition for this part?'

Claire grimaced. 'Oh, only about five hundred other starving hopefuls, I should think.'

Lynn laughed and shook her head. 'Honestly, Claire, you must have as good a chance as anybody. You have masses of talent. You must realise that or you wouldn't keep on trying as you have been doing, and you look so ...' She paused and laughed, raising her eyebrows expressively. 'What's the word I'm looking for?'

Claire grinned reluctantly at her. 'I don't know, but I've got an unpleasant feeling I'm going to hear it any minute.'

Lynn's expression was teasing. 'Sexy, that's definitely it!'

Claire's mobile features revealed her thoughts all too clearly and Lynn laughed again. 'An attractive appearance must help, surely?'

Claire moved her shoulders in a faint shrug. 'Maybe, but most directors are looking for much more than that, and those that aren't,' she shrugged again, 'I'm just not in the market for those kind of complications.'

Claire wanted to be successful, but as a result of her own efforts and not because some creepy director fancied going to bed with her. Even the thought made her shudder. That kind of life would be destructive. The lure of stardom was strong, but not strong enough for her to abandon her principles to attain it.

Lynn was still watching Claire's pensive face, a smile in her eyes. 'Some of those young directors are rather dishy,' she said.

'The ones who need to employ the casting couch don't come into that category, I can assure you.'

'But it's Jake Svenson who is directing this film, isn't it?' Lynn asked now. 'I saw him on television once, all dark and damn your eyes.' She stretched voluptuously. 'Lovely!'

It was Claire's turn to laugh. 'I don't know very much about the man but he can certainly pick his scripts. This one has got everything—adventure, love, violence. You name it.'

'Sex?' Lynn queried with delicately raised brows.

'That too,' Claire agreed, amusement still lingering in her voice. 'It's set in Cornwall in the late seventeenth century and concerns an entire village engaged in the wrecking and plundering of passing vessels. The story hinges on the fact that the wreckers always kill everyone who survives the actual destruction of their ship. Destroying the evidence so to speak.'

Lynn pulled a face. 'Charming!'

Claire shrugged expressively. 'It is rather gory, but anyway, on this occasion a young French girl does manage to reach the shore and is allowed to live by the young man who finds her. He falls in love with her and ultimately she becomes the bride of the title.' She paused, adjusting her position on the buffet, her feet hooked around the legs. 'There are a couple of big names in the cast already who should draw the crowds even if the story doesn't appeal overmuch; Richard Angrams plays the leader of the wreckers and Marianne Lejeune, the lady of the manor who falls in love with him. All good meaty stuff. Just pray that the casting director is susceptible to green-eyed red-heads.'

'I'm praying, Claire, believe me. It's time you had your fair share of success. God knows, you've worked hard enough.'

Claire turned the switch on the tape recorder with a decisive click and sat back on her heels with a sigh. She had been unable to resist listening one final time to the recorded voices with their heavy Cornish accents. She knew she had driven Lynn wild over the last few days, turning on the tape recorder at every opportunity, but at least she had the satisfaction of knowing that her accent was as good as she could possibly make it. Not that the knowledge had improved her self-confidence, far from it. She was so nervous that she found it impossible to concentrate on anything for more than a few minutes at a time.

It didn't help being on her own in the flat. Lynn had unexpectedly been offered a full day's modelling work with a knitwear firm and had had to be at the studio for eight-thirty. Claire was pleased for her, but she would have welcomed her company this morning. She sighed again and pushed the tape recorder to the side of the room. It was fortunate that Mike was coming to collect her. His company would surely calm her down a little.

She glanced briefly at her watch, giving a small exclamation of dismay as she realised that Mike would soon be arriving and she wasn't completely ready. She moved quickly into the bedroom, pausing in her stride as she passed the dressing-table mirror. She saw a tall girl dressed in cream linen trousers pleated at the waist and topped by a strawberry coloured silk blouse. It was an attractive reflection but she was in no mood to appreciate it; to her oversensitive eyes her colouring was far too vibrant, her figure too full-breasted, the large green eyes staring back at her from the mirror seeming to promise something that she was far from ready to fulfil.

She was still gazing dispiritedly at her image in the elderly, spotted mirror when the raucous blaring of a car horn brought her back to the present with a jolt. She gave a small, startled exclamation and rushed into the living room, sliding up the sash window with a bang, her hair blowing around her face like a silken banner as she stuck her head out into the street.

Mike had the hood of the old MG down as she guessed he would and she gave an inward groan. No use expecting to arrive at the audition looking composed and immaculate, the Wreck of the Hesperus would probably describe her more accurately. Mike glanced upwards, attracted by the sound of the opening window, smiling appreciatively at the glowing picture she presented.

'I won't be a minute,' she called, only waiting for his wave of acknowledgment before slamming the window shut again. Her coat was still in the bedroom and she rushed in to fetch it, reappearing almost immediately, her arms half-way into her old sheepskin, a woollen scarf clutched in one hand. The coat and scarf were donned in seconds and then she was through the door and on to the landing, pushing the key into her shoulder bag before plunging at top speed down the stairs to the ground floor.

They reached the audition with plenty of time to spare but even so the large, echoing hall was already bulging at the seams as Claire realised when she pushed open the swing doors and stepped slowly into the crowded room, her glance flickering disbelievingly around. She was sure that there must be at least fifty people present for every available role and her sinking spirits were mirrored in her dejected expression.

'Chin up,' Mike murmured into her ear. 'It could be worse.'

'Do you want to bet!' Claire stared round again, her mobile features expressing her incredulity. 'Personally I don't see how they could possibly squeeze anyone else into the room. We shall probably all die from asphyxiation as it is. Perhaps it's a new idea for depleting the acting population of the city.' Her green eyes were wide as she turned to Mike. 'Where do they all come from, for heaven's sake? I didn't know there were so many actors in the country.'

'All is not lost,' Mike stated cheerfully. He gestured towards a chattering crowd of women dressed in leotards and tights. 'I've just been eavesdropping and as far as I can understand it the casting is running late. Apparently it started at some unearthly hour this morning and at least half this crowd are auditioning for the dancing roles.' He turned to Claire. 'You know, the grand ball at the beginning of the film.'

'That only makes it a ratio of about one job for every thirty eager applicants then,' Claire replied with wry emphasis. 'School concerts were never like this.'

'Grouser,' Mike grinned. 'Go and take your coat off, Claire, and let's get our names down on the list. Maybe they'll tell us to go home and come back this afternoon.'

Claire raised her eyes heavenward. 'Why ever should they? They're not paying us. It's only our time they're wasting after all.' Then she laughed ruefully. 'Sorry, Mike! Grouser is right. I get so tense and nervous before these sessions that it makes me bad tempered.'

'Calm down then,' Mike admonished gently. 'Relax and you can't fail. One look and the casting director will be hooked, believe me.'

Claire cast him an old-fashioned glance. 'If only it was so easy. Are there really any impressionable casting directors left in this sophisticated world? In my experience they've seen it all.'

'But wouldn't say no to a private showing,' Mike added

with a wicked twinkle. 'Go on, Claire. Take your coat off and let's at least look as though we mean business.'

Claire scanned the crowded room as she returned from the cloakroom. There were a few familiar faces around. They seemed to crop up at all the same auditions. It was depressing really when she considered the situation. Would she still be doing the same old thing in ten years, fighting for any small part that was going? She thrust the unpleasant thought away angrily. She was determined to keep trying and if her career never got off the ground, well, at least she would have done her best and that was surely the important thing.

A fresh influx of bodies had surged into the room since she had left it and it was a moment before she saw Mike. He was standing where she had left him, but her heart sank like a stone when she recognised the all too familiar figure of Alan Crosby by his side. She hovered uncertainly by the door for a moment knowing she was being ridiculous. They were in the same profession after all and shared many of the same friends. She couldn't avoid him for ever! With the same sort of effort as a swimmer struggling against the tide she forced her unwilling legs to move forward, a smile fixed to her generous mouth.

He was deep in conversation with Mike but as she watched he raised his head and saw her, his brown eyes lightening perceptibly as he strode forward.

'Claire, darling, it's wonderful to see you.' He had gripped her shoulders and planted a warm kiss on her unresponsive mouth almost before she was aware of it. He stood back. 'You look as beautiful as always.'

'Th-thank you.' Claire was lost for words. What could she say? Despite their last angry confrontation Alan clearly hadn't realised that their relationship had ended and now was hardly a suitable time for explanations.

'H-have you been here long?' she managed to stammer. 'Mike and I just walked in a couple of minutes ago.'

Alan frowned, sensing the reserve in her manner. 'About half an hour.' He bent his tawny head. 'What's wrong, Claire? You're very quiet. You're not still angry with me, are you?'

This was the moment. Claire knew she had to tell him the truth. She took a deep breath.

'Did Alan tell you the glad news?'

Claire was ashamed to feel relief at Mike's cheerful interruption and her eyes turned to him with an eagerness she couldn't quite disguise. 'No, what is it?' she asked.

'Alan's been eavesdropping too and apparently the dancers and choreographer are to be transferred elsewhere, poor things.'

Mike's interruption hadn't pleased Alan and these words seemed to fuel his annoyance. 'The director's apparently arranged for a couple of double deckers to transfer the lot of them. And the quicker the better,' he said, his voice rising in irritation. 'I'm bloody sick of hanging around for hours at every audition. It's about time they decided to treat us more like human beings and less like a pack of sheep. We should all get together and try to do something about the situation. Half the people who work for these film companies need a bloody good kick up the pants.'

Claire and Mike exchanged glances. Alan was well known for his radical views but it did no good to voice them in a situation like the present one. And not all auditions were like this, they usually involved quite small numbers of people. At least Claire's agent had warned her what it would be like before she came. Her eyes moved rather nervously around the room. Already Alan's raised tones had attracted more than a few curious glances. She had noticed the two men talking quietly together in the open doorway when she first walked in. Somehow they didn't look like fellow hopefuls in the job stakes and Claire was uncomfortably aware that the taller of them had been taking an inordinate amount of interest in Alan's conversation.

She risked another glance. His icy blue eyes were still looking in their direction and she turned away again quickly, feeling ridiculously vulnerable. Tall and dark, his harsh features were certainly not conventionally handsome but he would attract attention in any gathering. The man's arrogance stood out a mile. She studied him again from beneath lowered lids. There was no doubt about it, he was still staring at her. Claire shivered suddenly, dropping her gaze. She had been stripped by men's eyes before and she had always loathed the sensation, but this man's probing gaze was something else again. Claire felt as though those arctic eyes had somehow managed to pierce her skull and read her every thought. She felt both naked and defenceless.

She took a shaky breath, wanting to turn and run, and then did just that, pushing her way purposefully down the crowded hall looking neither to the right nor the left, oblivious to Alan's muttered protests, only anxious to put as much distance as possible between herself and those cold, assessing eyes as she could. The more she thought about the man the more angry she became. How dare he look at her in that way! As though she was something unpleasant that the cat had dragged in. Sure, Alan's words had not been exactly tactful but they hadn't been entirely without foundation either. And if, as she suspected, he did work for the film company, instead of eavesdropping on their conversation he could have been far more usefully employed trying to speed up the casting process.

They were almost at the front of the hall before Claire's pace slackened. Both Mike and Alan had followed her, she realised. Alan looking flustered, Mike merely amused.

'Did you see your landlord back there?' he asked, his eyes teasing her in a way she always found hard to resist. 'I didn't realise you were quite so desperate for the rent.'

'Idiot!' Claire remarked with an answering grin. 'There was a man at the door positively drinking in every word that Alan uttered and I'm sure he must work for the film company.'

'So what? I meant every damned syllable!' Alan put in quickly, but no longer in quite such belligerent tones, Claire noticed with uncharacteristic cynicism.

'I know you did,' she agreed. 'But now is hardly the time to sound off about it. Not if you want a part in the film.'

Alan still looked angry and clearly he didn't care for any criticism of his actions, particularly not from Claire, but if he didn't agree with her words at least he made no immediate protest and Claire was free to look around her a little. The crush was almost as bad as ever even though the dancers had already left the room, and with a further resurgence of stage fright she realised that people were already being called for their auditions.

As relative late comers she and Mike were quite well down the list but the knowledge didn't calm her jangled nerves any. The only fortunate note in the proceedings being the fact that Alan's audition preceded both her own and Mike's. She hoped quite desperately that he would go home as soon as he had completed it. He was really getting her down today.

She watched his angry face surreptitiously for a moment as he continued to mutter in subdued tones to Mike. She made no attempt to listen to his words. She could tell the mood of his conversation from his expression. She didn't enjoy waiting herself, no one did, but she was sensible enough to be able to visualise the difficulties involved. She knew there had been problems in the production which had only just been ironed out, and filming was planned to start within a few weeks. It seemed like an impossible task.

'. . . it's absolutely disgraceful!'

Claire caught the tail end of Alan's conversation and deliberately shut her ears. Poor Mike, she thought. He must be bored to tears. She glanced his way. He was hiding it well. She knew that he and Alan had been friends since their schooldays. He was presumably accustomed to Alan's furious outbursts by now.

Yet another name being called on the tannoy system attracted Claire's attention and as she watched a tall, willowy brunette appeared out of the press of people and walked towards the door in one corner of the hall. She looked beautifully calm and composed and Claire wished that she could muster half that girl's self-confidence.

The actual auditions were being held in a smaller room at one side of the hall and she tried to calm herself with the thought that at least there wouldn't be a large audience to witness her performance, and there were ten female roles to fill. Surely she ought to have a chance. Think positive, she told herself sternly, but it was difficult to ignore the fact that her hands were already clammy with sweat and her legs felt like jelly. She sat quietly, struggling to maintain a brave façade, and when Alan's name was called she managed to wish him luck quite cheerfully. He clearly wasn't affected by pre-audition nerves, she realised as she watched his departing back. The confident set of his broad shoulders said all there was to say about his state of mind.

It seemed very quiet when he had gone but his powerful frame reappeared in the doorway across the hall long before Claire had expected to see him. He didn't look pleased and she watched his approach with anxious green eyes.

'No joy!' He slouched on to the seat beside her, looking furious. 'There were three guys in there and they were all so damned busy talking among themselves they barely listened to my reading.'

Claire couldn't blame him for being angry. She sat fidgeting nervously on the wooden bench, chewing her bottom lip until it hurt. She had been worried before, but Alan's experience was the final straw. It was hot in the room too, hundreds of sweating bodies raising the temperature to unreasonable levels. She could feel her head beginning to spin and pushed herself shakily to her feet. Mike's head turned as she tottered on to her high heels and he was on his feet, his supporting hand beneath her elbow in an instant.

'My God, Claire, you look terrible!'

She grimaced weakly. 'Thanks a million.' And then shook her head, bronze curls flying, forcing a shaky laugh. 'Don't worry, it's just my stupid stage fright as usual.'

'Do you want me to try and get you something? A glass of water, perhaps? Or there's a woman selling coffee in the corridor.'

He was still looking concerned but Claire shook her head again. 'No, I just need some fresh air, that's all. It's so close in here.'

'I'll come out with you,' Mike offered immediately. 'It is stuffy in here and it wouldn't do me any harm to stretch my legs.'

Alan had just been standing watching them but now he moved to Claire's side. 'I'm going out now anyway. I'll go with Claire.'

'We'll all go,' Mike remarked cheerfully.

'There's no need, I'll see to Claire.'

Alan was very insistent and Claire only caught a glimpse of the look he flung at Mike, but it was enough. Clearly he intended a tête-à-tête and she just couldn't cope, not today.

She turned to him rather desperately. 'It's kind of you, but honestly I'd prefer you not to bother. I'll be okay, I promise. It would do me good to be alone for a while.'

She could have saved her breath.

He gave her a perfunctory smile. 'Don't fuss woman. I'm coming with you.'

He was shrugging his shoulders into his waterproof jacket as he spoke. Claire was fairly certain that he hadn't listened to a word she'd said. He wanted to come out with her and that was that. He was an insensitive swine, she decided now. But short of a full-scale scene in the middle of the packed hall there seemed to be no way she could avoid him. She couldn't repress a sigh, but she moved her shoulders in a vaguely acquiescent gesture. 'Okay,' she murmured, 'if you want to come.' She left it at that. She felt far too shaky to enter into an argument. She turned to Mike. 'I won't be long,' she told him.

He nodded, his eyes sympathetic. 'Take care.' Claire had told him that she and Alan had quarrelled. He must guess how she was feeling, but there was nothing that he could do. She meekly allowed Alan to take her arm and followed him down the length of the hall and out of the room.

CHAPTER TWO

THE two men whose presence by the door had so disturbed Claire had disappeared by now and she heaved a silent sigh of relief. She hadn't looked forward to making her exit under their icy stares, particularly not with Alan's fingers gripping her elbow so possessively. He was making it impossible for her to escape and yet she longed desperately for a period of quiet reflection. It was so important for her to give a good audition.

She was so completely absorbed in her own thoughts that they were into the corridor and past the outer door almost before she was aware of it. Alan's fingers still held her tightly but now she hung back, aware that the situation was going to be even more difficult than she had anticipated.

'I told you, I need to get some fresh air,' she cried. 'This isn't the way out of the building.'

'I want to talk to you, Claire. It won't take long.' As Alan spoke he continued to urge her along. Claire didn't want to go, but what could she do? He was stronger than she was and his hard fingers gripped her upper arm in a very determined fashion. She stared at his handsome profile resentfully as he hustled her along, wondering how she could ever have fancied herself in love with him. He was a self-centred beast, she decided. He hadn't even asked her how she was feeling. It had been Mike who had shown all the concern.

It would no doubt be all the same to him if she keeled over in a dead faint in the middle of the corridor. He would probably just drag her along, feet first into a suitable corner and wait until she came round to have his little conversation. The mental picture this thought conjured up made her want to giggle and her mobile

24

mouth twitched slightly at the corners. Not that there was the smallest fear of her passing out, she realised with relief. In fact she felt almost capable of tackling Alan and insisting that he let her return to the hall.

It was probably only a couple of minutes since they had left it but to Claire they seemed to have been walking for hours. She couldn't imagine where Alan was taking her and she hung back deliberately so he had to slow his pace. He turned, a trace of irritation on his features.

'I'd like to go back,' she insisted. 'I'm feeling much better.'

'This won't take a minute.' He smiled persuasively. 'I thought if we could find an empty room somewhere you would be able to sit and relax for a few minutes.'

'I would prefer to go back to the hall,' Claire insisted quietly.

'No need.' As Claire had been speaking Alan had pushed open one of the doors leading into the corridor and he turned to her now with the air of a magician conjuring a rabbit out of a hat. 'We can go in here.' He widened the gap and signed for her to enter but she wouldn't.

'I don't think we ought to go in.' She turned to face him. He was trying to bully her as usual and she didn't like it. 'We're trespassing as it is, and I'm sure we oughtn't to be wandering around the building like this.'

'What possible objection could there be?' Alan was all sweet reason as he tried to show Claire, in the nicest possible way, just how idiotic she was being. 'Don't be such a frightened rabbit. Nobody is going to come in here.' He shrugged. 'And even if they did, what then? I doubt if there's anything worth stealing in the entire building.'

Claire still hesitated in the doorway. 'I don't like it.' She knew she was inclined to be timid at times and she knew that her timidity irritated Alan, but reluctance to trespass wasn't her only objection. For one thing she didn't want to be alone with him. Not that she had any intention of telling him that. Instead she sighed heavily, 'It just isn't sensible to shut ourselves away in here. We could go back and stand outside the hall. You could still talk to me without being overheard. What if my name is called for the audition? Mike would never find me here.'

'You'll have ages to wait,' Alan assured her quickly. 'I've just got to talk to you, Claire. I can't go on like this any longer.'

His hand slid from her elbow to grasp her cold fingers, urging her into the room and Claire obeyed him helplessly. Alan closed the door behind them with a decisive click and Claire had a moment in which to look around her. Her heart sank, there were piles of coats and jackets thrown carelessly over an old table in the centre of the room. She turned to Alan, anxiety giving a sharp edge to her tones. 'We should never have come in here. The room's being used as a cloakroom. If anyone comes in it will look as though we've been rifling coat pockets.'

Alan laughed in a way that jarred Claire's nerves. 'My God! The girl's fussing about a pile of old coats when I'm trying to tell her that I love her.' He bent his head, drawing her fingers to his lips and kissing them passionately.

Even had she returned his love the moment would have been ill chosen. She tried to tug her fingers away but he held on to them tightly. 'Alan,' she cried. 'I want to leave. Can't you understand that? We're trespassing, and I for one have no intention of being discovered in here.' She turned towards the door. 'I'm leaving, whether you come or not.' She made to brush past him but he grabbed her arm.

'I've got to talk to you, Claire,' he insisted huskily.

She tried to prise his fingers apart although to her shame her own hand trembled slightly. She told herself she was being ridiculous. This is Alan, an old friend. She knew she had no need to be afraid of him and yet she couldn't prevent that faint twinge of unease as she saw the way he was staring at her.

'Not now, Alan, please,' she begged. 'I must get back for my audition.'

'Damn your audition!' he stated harshly. 'I love you, Claire. Can't you see that?'

Claire could feel her temper rising and she tried again to pull her arm from his grasp. 'I don't believe that you do love me. If you did you would be trying to help me get this part, not standing in my way.'

'Our relationship's a damned sight more important than this film.'

'Maybe to you, Alan, but not to me, and if it was your audition that was still to come I think you would be viewing the situation in a totally different light.'

Claire regretted her words the moment she'd uttered them. Alan's jaw tightened angrily and his hands slid from her upper arms to grip her shoulders tightly. He was hurting her.

'Let me go,' she protested. 'You're being ridiculous!'

He seemed not to hear her but stared at her with tormented eyes. 'Kiss me, Claire,' he muttered thickly. 'Tell me that you still love me.'

She moved her head desperately from side to side in an effort to escape his searching mouth. 'Let me go, Alan!' she cried again. 'Don't do this!' She was pinioned against the edge of the table by his hard body. He wanted her, there was no doubt about that, but she felt repelled by his desire, and afraid. She hated him to touch her like this!

With a sudden violent heave she wrenched herself half out of his arms, but he was too quick and too strong for her and he hauled her back towards his body with scant regard for the bruisable quality of her flesh. She heard the fine silk of her blouse tear beneath his fingers but she barely heeded it. Her struggles had not weakened his hold in the slightest. She opened her mouth to protest once more and with a small sound of triumph his lips closed over her own. She fought against that kiss with all her strength, marvelling that she had once enjoyed being in this man's arms. She hated him!

She had been a fool to trust him, but it was too late for such thoughts.

She didn't even hear the door fly open she was so intent on her own silent struggle. She only knew that for a brief moment Alan had relaxed his iron grip. This was her chance. She was out of his arms and across the room in a couple of strides, flinging a hasty backward glance at Alan's frozen figure as she went. That backward glance was her undoing. She came to a sudden, jarring halt, the obstacle in her path large and immovable and smelling faintly of expensive aftershave. Her arms were taken in a grip that was almost as painful as Alan's had been and she raised shocked, green eyes to the familiar dark-browed face that seemed to be towering over her.

'Oh no, not you again!' The exclamation was out before she could prevent it and for a moment shock held her rigid as a pair of cold blue eyes bored into her skull. His expression made her tremble. It would never be a gentle face, she realised fleetingly. The angles were too sharp for that, his nose too large and high-bridged for symmetry, but at this moment it looked as though it had been carved out of ice.

'Who are you? What the hell are you doing here?' He shot the questions at her like bullets from a gun, his voice deep and harsh, his gaze barely flickering over Alan's still figure before he returned the full force of those glacial orbs to Claire's pale features.

Claire answered him automatically. His commanding manner demanded to be obeyed. 'No-nothing at all. We weren't doing anything.' To her shame her voice was trembling, in fact she was trembling all over and it took an immense effort of will to hold up her chin and meet his eyes. His own were openly contemptuous as they moved slowly over her dishevelled figure. They made her overwhelmingly aware of the white skin of her shoulder peeping through the tear in her blouse and the buttons loosened in that last furious struggle.

But that raw contempt had the opposite effect from

the one he intended. It made her angry. It was either that or tears and she was damned if she was going to give this hateful man the satisfaction of seeing her cry. Her own lips tightened and her chin went up another notch.

'Let me go,' she demanded. She tried to pull away but he was holding her too tightly,

'I'll let you go when I'm good and ready and that won't be until you've given me a good explanation for your presence in this room.'

She knew they looked suspicious. Hadn't she said so herself? And in normal circumstances she would have been suitably apologetic, offering her momentary illness as an explanation for their presence, but one look at his face had told her that no explanation of hers would be believed. She had already been tried and condemned and she had no intention of pleading with him.

She took a deep breath. 'I'm sure you can guess why we came in here,' she murmured. 'We wanted somewhere quiet where we could make love. This seemed as good a place as any.' And then very slowly she began to fasten the torn buttons of her blouse, holding his gaze, a faintly insolent smile curving her lips.

Alan gave a choked exclamation but she ignored it, all her attention focused on the tall, dark stranger still gripping her arms. He didn't disappoint her. He stared at her as though he couldn't believe his eyes and then shook his head, an expression of disgust crossing his lean features.

'My God! I had you taped as trouble the moment I set eyes on you and I was right!'

'There's no law against sex, is there?' Claire gave him back stare for stare, her temper thoroughly roused. She knew perfectly well she was behaving outrageously but he was so arrogant, why should she regret anything she said to him?

He ignored her deliberate provocation, his eyes flicking from her to Alan and back again. 'Who are you?' he rapped out. 'Where do you come from? If you provide me with positive identification I might consider letting you leave, but not otherwise.'

Did he really think he could keep them there if they chose to leave, Claire wondered angrily. There was no end to the arrogance of the man. She spoke again, making no secret of her feelings. 'As I said, we aren't doing any damage. I don't see why you're so keen to interfere!'

He glared down at her, blue eyes flashing. 'This is a private room, lady, and you and lover boy over there are trespassing.'

'Ring for the police, why don't you? I'm sure they would be interested,' Claire replied, her tones scathing.

'Perhaps I will at that!'

'Do if you want to.' Claire's eyes met and challenged his. 'You can even search me if you don't believe what I say.'

His lip curled. 'Thank you, that won't be necessary.' He had been gripping her shoulders but now he dropped his hands as though he couldn't bear to touch her.

'For God's sake, Claire!' Alan spoke for the first time, clearly bewildered by her behaviour, but Claire scarcely heard him, now that she was free she realised that she had enjoyed the purely physical sensation of being in the hateful man's arms. She was overwhelmingly aware of the height and the breadth of him. Reluctantly she acknowledged that she would have liked him to touch her again, and this made her angrier than ever, her thoughts and emotions in such complete turmoil that she missed most of Alan's apology.

'We came in for a quiet talk,' he was saying now. 'Claire was nervous before her audition. She needed to get away from the crowds. We're sorry if we inadvertently trespassed.'

'I'm not sorry,' Claire interposed swiftly.

The stranger's eyes were chips of ice. 'Be careful, lady! Be very careful!' he warned in dangerously quiet tones.

'We are sorry,' Alan insisted anxiously. 'We had no intention of trespassing. It's as I told you, Claire was nervous before her audition. We would be happy to give you our names and addresses if that would help. I have my driving licence somewhere.' He was fishing in his breast pocket now, all eagerness to please. A massive *volte face* from his earlier belligerence, Claire thought with faint contempt.

But his action had given her the opportunity she needed. The stranger's attention had withdrawn from her for the moment and before she really had time to consider whether her action was a sensible one, she had turned on her heel and whisked around his tall figure, making a dash for the door, slamming it firmly behind her, the impetus of her own escape carrying her on wobbly legs at full speed down the corridor and back towards the people, the lights and the chatter in the crowded hall.

Mike was on his feet anxiously scanning the open doorway when she reached it and his face broke into a relieved smile as soon as he saw her threading her way rather unsteadily through the chattering groups of people towards him.

'Thank God you're here! I've been having a fit! I've been all over the building looking for you. I was afraid you were going to miss your audition.'

Claire's green eyes were wide and anxious. 'Have they called my name?'

He took her hands, squeezing her fingers reassuringly. 'No, don't look so worried. You're in time.'

Claire let out her breath on a trembling sigh. 'Thank the Lord for that anyway!' She would get her chance! Although she couldn't quite believe it. Not after all that had happened.

Mike's voice interrupted her worried thoughts. 'Where have you been, Claire? If it isn't a rude question. I looked everywhere and I couldn't see you.'

Claire shook her head, bronze curls tumbling. 'Don't ask, Mike, just don't ask!'

'For God's sake, love, you're trembling like a leaf.' He took a closer look at the creamy pallor of her complexion. 'I thought you were going outside to calm your nerves. It certainly doesn't seem to have been very effective.'

Claire laughed with mounting hysteria as she remembered the situation from which she'd just escaped. 'You can say that again!'

'Calm down, Claire!'

'I'm trying! I'm really trying! But one thing's for sure, I'm definitely off men at the moment—fat ones, thin ones . . .'

'Thanks a million.' Mike's grimace was half amused, half wry.

Claire turned to him. 'Not you, Mike. Never you! It's Alan. I could just about murder him! How I could . . .'

Claire stiffened, the sudden announcement stunning her into silence, and then: 'Say I was hearing things, Mike. Tell me that voice was a figment of my overheated imagination,' she moaned.

Mike's eyes were sympathetic. 'I'm afraid not, my love. It was definitely your name he called.'

'But I'm not ready,' Claire wailed. 'I need to comb my hair . . . and my blouse is torn. God, I must look a sight! I can't go in like this, I just can't!'

Mike gripped her by the shoulders and turned her around, his eyes moving swiftly and assessingly over her figure. 'You look delicious,' he said at length, his eyes smiling reassurance into hers. 'Good enough to eat!'

'I know . . . a carrot,' Claire sighed, smiling in spite of herself.

He laughed. 'Did I say that? No . . . honestly, Claire, you look fine.'

'Claire Grant!' her name boomed out once again and Claire had great difficulty in preventing herself from running screaming out of the hall.

She turned her head, her eyes wide and frightened. 'Do I look okay, Mike, honestly? What about my blouse?' She touched the small tear with her fingers. 'Does this show?'

'You look fantastic ... and believe me, no one is going to notice that unless you point it out to them. Now, just take deep breaths as Uncle Mike tells you and start walking. Go on!' He urged, giving her a gentle push in the small of the back. 'And good luck!'

Claire stumbled along on shaking legs trying desperately to compose herself. The door to the audition room faced her all too quickly, tightly closed, giving no clue to the situation awaiting her behind its wooden panels. She took a deep, steadying breath as Mike had recommended and glanced hastily down at the front of her blouse. All her buttons were intact and securely fastened and Mike was right, the tear barely showed. She heaved another trembling breath. Damn Alan Crosby! She was frightened enough without the additional worry of knowing she looked a mess.

Before she could change her mind she forced herself to raise a trembling hand and tap tentatively on the door. A voice called for her to enter and she turned the handle and walked inside, closing it with quivering fingers behind her. Her eyes flickered nervously around the room. There wasn't much to see. It was very small, the only illumination coming from the strip light on the ceiling. Clearly there were windows but these were covered with heavy curtains. It looked gloomy and depressing and Claire shivered involuntarily.

The brief appraisal had only taken a second and now her eyes flew to the man behind the rather battered desk. He was already on his feet, his smile warm and friendly. Could this be the fabled Jake Svenson, Claire wondered. But no, he couldn't possibly be. How had Lynn described the director? Dark and damn your eyes! This man was small and rather plump, his hair already beginning to recede at the temples. But he looked friendly and that was a great relief.

She walked nervously towards his outstretched hand and he took her fingers in a firm clasp: 'Sit down, Miss Grant,' he advised her kindly, returning to his own chair behind the desk.

This was nothing like Claire had expected. Where were Alan's three interviewers who talked almost non-stop throughout his audition? Had they really existed, Claire wondered, or were they just an excuse he had invented because he hadn't been offered a job? It would be just like him, Claire decided, with a resurgence of her earlier anger. He wouldn't have cared that the story might upset herself and Mike. Not if it suited his purpose. The man behind the desk was speaking, she realised with a sudden jolt and she pulled her wandering thoughts back on track with an effort.

He was smiling at her warmly. 'My name is Dave Tillson. I shall be helping to direct the film.' He relaxed back into his chair, his hands clasped over his stomach. 'In fact my official title is First Assistant Director.' He smiled again, more broadly. 'General dogsbody might describe me more aptly.'

Claire couldn't help smiling back. He really was a sweetie. Already she could feel her self-confidence returning under his calming influence.

'So . . .' He shuffled the papers on his desk and gave her another smile, appreciating the glowing picture she made, her hair tumbling in bronze profusion around her shoulders, an unaccustomed tinge of pink colouring her pale skin. 'I would like you to read a short passage from the script, Miss Grant. I shall play the masculine role.' He pushed a few typed and stapled sheets across the desk towards her. 'Read the script through before we start. Take your time.'

Claire nodded briefly. 'Thank you,' she murmured nervously, her eyes already moving over the typed pages. She scanned them quickly, trying to make some sense of the words which danced in front of her eyes. But it was hopeless. She just couldn't concentrate. A pair of arctic blue eyes had returned to haunt her. She forced herself to read one word at a time. She was being ridiculous, allowing the infuriating stranger to disturb her at such a moment. He appeared to have been dogging her footsteps with malevolent insistence the entire morning. Was there no way she could escape him?

With a start she realised that time was passing and she still had half the script to read. Her eyes quickly began to scan the print again. Thank goodness she had done so much work on her Cornish accent, that at least was one thing the director wouldn't be able to fault. She cast an uncertain glance towards him. He was apparently completely absorbed in the papers littering the desk in front of him. Claire wondered whether she would have time to read through the script again. Certainly she hadn't taken much in at the beginning, but then it was too late. He raised his head from the desk.

'Ready, Miss Grant?'

Claire wanted to say that no, she would never be ready but instead she nodded, dry mouthed. She had barely uttered a word since she entered the room, she realised and she began to wonder if she was capable of speech any longer. She bent her head, opened her mouth to speak and her worst fears were realised. Her voice came out an indistinguishable croak. She knew she was blushing a fiery red and kept her head down to hide it, bronze-red hair falling forward over her face.

'I'm—I'm sorry, Mr Tillson. I'm a litttle . . . nervous. Could I start again do you think?'

'Of course,' he agreed instantly. 'Would it help if you stood up to read? Maybe you could get the feel of the part more easily.'

Claire nodded gratefully and rose to her feet. She paused a moment, moistening her dry lips with her tongue. This is your big chance, Claire Grant, she told herself sternly. Don't louse it up at this stage.

'I don't know who has told you but it's just not true,' she wailed, her voice gaining strength as her confidence grew. Her accent was stilted, she realised, but at least it was accurate and she could feel herself loosening up as the words flowed more easily from her tongue. 'Why won't you believe me?' she cried and then stopped in mid stream in response to Dave Tillson's lifted hand. The door had opened behind her and she turned her head automatically to look, almost groaning aloud at what she saw. She could hardly believe her eyes. Not only had the dark stranger continued to disturb her thoughts in that exasperating way, but he was here in person, relaxed and completely at ease, one shoulder resting indolently on the closed door, his cold blue eyes mocking Claire's evident confusion.

'So, the elusive Miss Grant.' He smiled in a way that made her want to hit him, but still she couldn't help staring. He was quite the sexiest individual that she had ever encountered. Tall and dark, his jeans and leather jacket fitting him like a second skin, he watched Claire with equal intensity, his eyes moving over her body with insulting thoroughness, roving from breast to thigh to the long curving length of her legs and back again, bringing the colour surging to her cheeks and an angry sparkle to her eyes. He knew exactly what he was doing, she realised impotently and there wasn't a damned thing she could do about it!

'Do you know Miss Grant?' Dave Tillson's puzzled tones interrupted her angry thoughts. 'I would have waited if I'd realised that you wanted to be in at her audition.'

Claire watched with angry eyes as the intruder levered himself from his position by the door and strolled casually across the room towards the desk, lowering himself on to one corner, his foot swinging idly. He glanced across at Claire with another deliberately mocking smile.

'I don't know her ... not intimately. In fact today was the occasion of our first meeting.'

Claire took an instinctive step forward. 'And our last too, I hope!'

He seemed amused rather than angered by Claire's provocative answer. He smiled again and Claire clenched her fingers tightly by her side.

'Oh, I think I can definitely promise you that.'

Without hurrying he reached into his jacket pocket and extracted a packet of cigarettes, taking one himself before offering them to Dave. Claire suspected that he knew just how awkward she felt, standing in the middle of the room, clutching the abandoned script in one hand. This was his way of making her suffer for her earlier misdemeanours and unfortunately he had all the right ammunition. But she was determined not to give him further cause for complaint, not in front of Dave Tillson anyway, and she clenched her teeth tightly on the angry words that longed to come spilling out.

Still he hadn't finished, she realised, as he leaned forward slowly, his dark hair falling over his forehead and lit first Dave Tillson's cigarette and then his own. Claire felt that she would burst into angry tears if they didn't speak to her soon. She just had to know what was going to happen to her. She eyed the assistant director uncertainly. Even he seemed to have completely forgotten her.

'I have seen three possibles,' he was saying. 'Although none of them were ideal.'

'Shall I start to read again, Mr Tillson?' Claire's voice sounded hoarse and uncertain, but at least she had claimed the assistant director's attention.

'Miss Grant, forgive me!' he replied immediately. 'We're being very rude.' He shot a questioning glance to the man at his side. 'I feel sure we're ready to hear you now.'

The dark man shook his head slowly, his eyes on Claire, cold and harsh and very blue. 'I'm not ready to hear, Miss Grant,' he stated abruptly. 'I shall never be ready. I already know she's unsuitable.'

Claire bit her lip, her eyes moving from one man to the other. Dave Tillson was already looking uncertain, but she wouldn't allow him to dismiss her without a fight, she just wouldn't. She took one shaky step forward, and then another until she reached the desk, her palms flat on the grainy suface, overwhelmingly conscious of the silent figure on her left but determinedly ignoring him.

She looked at Dave Tillson with pleading green eyes. 'Don't listen to him, please,' she begged. 'We had a difference of opinion earlier today it's true. Maybe the things I said to him weren't altogether tactful,' Claire admitted, knowing she was understating the case, but then she remembered the way he had stared at her earlier and she put up her head, the light of battle in her eyes. 'But he was very rude to me,' she said. 'And our argument certainly doesn't affect my ability as an actress.'

'You're a troublemaker, Miss Grant,' her tormentor put in harshly. 'You can go and louse up someone else's production if they're fool enough to employ you, but you sure as hell aren't going to cause trouble on my set.'

The full implication of his words didn't sink into Claire's brain immediately. She was still too busy trying to plead her cause with Dave Tillson. 'I'm not a troublemaker, Mr Tillson, I swear it, and I am a good actress. Give me a chance, please!' Claire couldn't keep the pleading note out of her voice.

Dave Tillson looked at her and then away again, shifting uncomfortably in his seat. He glanced towards the man at his side. 'I would like to give her a chance.'

'No way! She gets in this over my dead body!'

A glimmer of a smile entered Dave Tillson's eyes. 'I thought I was being given a free hand with the casting at this level? Essential experience, didn't you say?'

Claire understood at last. Her mouth dropped open and she shut it again quickly. What a blind fool she had been! Dear God, this could only have happened to her! This was the director! This cold, mocking individual was Lynn's dreamboat. There was certainly nothing faintly dream-inspiring about him today. Nightmares maybe! There was a distinct glint of steel in his eyes as he stared at the assistant director.

'Well, do we go my way or yours?' Dave Tillson was asking, meeting the director's gaze steadily.

Claire had no idea what passed between them in that

exchange of glances, she only knew she was holding her breath. There was a moment's pregnant silence and then with a startling change of mood a self-derisory grin twisted Jake Svenson's lips. 'Okay, okay, you win.' He smiled again. 'This will remind me never to make rash promises.'

With a sudden release of tension Dave Tillson sank back against his seat. 'Not rash, man, merely sensible. You know you can always rely on my judgment.'

Claire let out her pent breath on a faint, audible sigh. She was going to get her chance after all. Both men's heads swivelled towards her, Jake Svenson's grin disappearing like magic.

'It would appear that you have won for the present, Miss Grant,' he remarked unpleasantly. 'And we are about to have the unalloyed pleasure of hearing you read the script.'

Claire flushed vividly, her skin burning. His words had hurt, but she wouldn't allow him to see that. Instead she deliberately turned her back on him, forcing a warm smile to her lips as she addressed the assistant director. 'I'm sorry I asked you to stick your neck out for me,' she murmured sweetly.

He sat forward in his chair, his smile as uncomplicated and friendly as ever. 'Don't worry about it, Miss Grant,' he told her kindly. 'I think my neck can stand the strain. Now, how about it? Do you think you can read the script for me?'

'Yes, oh yes!' Claire was effusive in her thanks, but less pleased when she discovered that Jake Svenson was to read the part of her screen lover. Even so the audition went well. She put herself heart and soul into the role of the young girl accused of being unfaithful by her lover. She could almost feel the texture of the sand between her bare toes and hear the seagulls wheeling and crying above her head.

She was half aware of Jake Svenson standing in front of her, but he didn't, as she had expected, try to distract her in any way. He read the role of her angry

lover beautifully. She was almost sorry when it ended.
And the moment she closed her lips on the final word
she came back to reality with a jolt. Nothing had
changed. The director still disliked her. He would never
give her a part in his film however well she had read!

She raised tormented green eyes from the script and
they flew automatically to his face. He was watching
her with a disturbingly intent gaze, a cigarette clamped
between his lips, his blue eyes narrowed against the
wreathing smoke. She could read nothing in that
shuttered face. She turned to Dave Tillson and his
expression was equally as unrevealing. The fear and
tension which had vanished during her brief performance, came rushing back with renewed force. Perhaps
she'd made a hash of it after all! How the director must
be gloating! She wiped her damp palms surreptitiously
on the seat of her trousers. The silence seemed to be
going on and on, she wanted to scream, do anything to
break it.

'Sit down again for a moment,' Dave Tillson advised
at last.

Claire's knees were knocking as she lowered herself
on to the chair in front of the desk. Both men were
watching her so intently. Jake Svenson's jean-clad legs
only a few inches away from her face.

The assistant director leaned forward now, his fingers
steepled on the desk in front of him. 'You've obviously
studied your Cornish accent very thoroughly. Do you
come from that area?'

'No, from Manchester actually.'

'I was very impressed.'

Claire flushed with pleasure. She guessed that he was
only being kind. Letting her down lightly, but still it
was satisfying to receive praise of any sort.

He was quiet for a moment as though hesitating, and
then he seemed to make up his mind. 'I would like you
to read something else for me,' He reached into the
drawer at his side and withdrew another stapled section
of the typescript. 'I want to hear you read the part of

Désirée, the French girl shipwrecked on the Cornish coast. It's much more challenging, but I shall be able to judge your performance with greater accuracy.' He smiled. 'Are you agreeable?'

'Yes, yes, of course.' Claire's voice was husky with nerves but she took the script from his hand and clutched it tightly in her lap. She didn't understand why Dave Tillson was doing this but she did know she was being given another chance and she was going to grab it with both hands. The director still hadn't said a word, which puzzled her. She cast him another surreptitious glance. He was still smoking, apparently completely detached from the proceedings, but Claire sensed that the detachment was a façade. He looked icy and dangerous even in his present relaxed pose and she gave a tiny involuntary shiver.

'Read the script through, Miss Grant.' Dave Tillson's words pierced her reverie. 'Don't worry too much about the French accent,' he was saying reassuringly. 'Just get the correct emotion into the speech.'

Claire nodded weakly and bent her head, her hair falling forward across her cheek. It was hard to resist the impulse to cower behind its silken curtain. Jake Svenson's eyes were boring into her skull. Maybe he had sensed her looking at him, but whatever the reason she certainly had his full attention now. She was finding it amazingly difficult to concentrate, amazingly difficult to breathe even.

She forced herself to read the words on the page in front of her. She would need all her wits about her. Dave Tillson had been right. It was a much more difficult role. When she finally raised her eyes again it was to find the director also purposefully flicking through a copy of the script. Claire bent her head. She didn't want him to play the part of her lover. Not again. She didn't quite know why. She just knew a strange reluctance to speak the words of love written in the script.

The second reading began disastrously. Claire's

French accent was appalling. It grated on her ears. She struggled for a couple of pages but she knew she couldn't go on. She shook her head, controlling her voice with an effort.

'I'm sorry, Mr Tillson, I just can't do this. I don't know why.'

'Try again and pretend the woman's English.'

Claire's startled eyes flew to the director's face. Was she hearing things or was he actually trying to be helpful? Surprise made her speechless and her eyes flew back to Dave Tillson. When he nodded encouragingly she wasted no more time but began to read again. This time it worked. She was Désirée de Bourgogne. She even found a trace of accent creeping in without effort. And when the script called for her to clasp her lover's hand she found that her own hand reached out automatically towards Jake Svenson and he took it and held it fast in his own.

And then it was over. She was back in the small audition room. She was exhausted. She would have welcomed the director's supporting hand in that moment but he had jerked it away the moment they finished speaking so she simply stood and shivered helplessly.

'Thank you, Miss Grant.' Dave Tillson rose to his feet and smiled at her kindly.

This was it then, Claire thought wearily. This was where her bubble burst. They were dismissing her. Dave Tillson was still speaking and her anxious eyes flew to his face.

'I asked if Glendower was still your agent,' he repeated gently seeing the bewilderment in her expression. He looked down at the file on his desk. 'That's the information we have here.'

'Y-yes he is,' Claire agreed.

'Then we'll be in touch with him later. I am sure you realise that it's impossible for us to give a definite decision at this moment.'

'O-of course,' Claire stammered. So Dave Tillson at

least had liked her performance. It made it worse somehow, knowing that. If only she hadn't earned the director's dislike she might have been offered a part.

The assistant director held out his hand and Claire returned the clasp of his fingers with creditable composure. 'We'll be in touch, Miss Grant,' he promised quietly and Claire smiled gratefully as though she really believed that he could prevail against Jake Svenson's openly expressed hostility.

She would have liked to have left without any further recognition of his tormenting presence but her innate sense of politeness simply wouldn't allow it. The nod she received in reply to her 'Goodbye, Mr Svenson,' was cool in the extreme and his own 'Goodbye, Miss Grant,' sounded frighteningly final. By then Claire was almost past caring. Resigned to the fact that there would be no part for her in *Wrecker's Bride*. Only thankful to escape from that room and from Jake Svenson's steady blue gaze, surveying her so coldly.

CHAPTER THREE

CLAIRE climbed the stairs to the first floor feeling as though she was carrying the problems of the world on her slim shoulders. She had been given the chance that she craved and it had blown up in her face through no fault of her own. She had been reliving the day's events over and over again on her way home in the car wondering if there was any way she could have averted the disasters that had occurred.

In fact the phrase which recurred most frequently in her tangled thoughts was, 'If only'. If only Alan hadn't attended the audition. If only she had stayed safely in the hall with Mike. If only the director hadn't appeared like an evil genie at the start of her audition. She reached the landing and turned slowly towards the door of the flat, wondering how she was going to break the news to Lynn. They needed the money this part would have offered. It was as simple as that.

She sighed and slipped her key into the lock, pushing open the door with reluctance. Lynn was sitting beside the gas fire, her long legs tucked beneath her on the armchair, the standard lamp throwing a golden halo around her blonde head. She was reading but she raised her eyes the moment Claire entered the room. Claire didn't need to speak, one look at her face was obviously enough.

'You didn't get it?'

Claire shook her head. 'Don't call us, we'll call you.' She sighed, dropping her bag on to the floor at her feet and hanging her dripping sheepskin on to the hook at the back of the door. 'The weather certainly suits my mood. We were soaked through coming home. There's something wrong with the hood on the MG so I just cowered behind the windscreen and hoped for the best.'

Lynn rose to her feet, her face reflecting her concern. 'Not a very effective best by the look of you.' She moved towards her friend and stood watching her in exasperation. 'Oh Claire! What am I going to do with you? You'll catch your death! You're drenched to the skin! Your hair's dripping and you ought to change those trousers right away.'

Claire pulled a small face. 'Don't fuss, Lynn. I shall be all right, honestly.' She began to move towards the fire but Lynn stopped her.

'Go and change your trousers first. You can dry your hair in front of the fire after that. Go on,' she urged. 'And I'll put the kettle on while you're changing.'

Claire hurried out of her wet clothes, shivering a little in the unheated chill of the bedroom. She glanced out of the window at the pouring rain. It was only three-thirty but it was already necessary to turn on the lights. She had told Lynn that the weather matched her mood and it was true, she could have sat down at the dressing table and wept like a baby. Not that that would have improved the situation, she realised, quickly pulling on an old pair of jeans and shrugging a warm sweater over her silk blouse, but maybe it would have helped to relieve her feelings. She didn't know which emotion was uppermost in her mind; sheer frustration at a series of unhappy accidents, anger at Alan Crosby and Jake Svenson or sheer, unadulterated self-pity.

She hung her soaking trousers over a hanger and carried them into the living room with her. In her absence Lynn had closed the curtains and the room looked warm and welcoming. Already her depression had lifted somewhat and when Lynn walked out of the kitchen carrying two steaming mugs of coffee Claire managed a reassuring smile in answer to Lynn's searching glance. Not that Lynn looked totally reassured. She made Claire sit in front of the fire and then handed her a mug of coffee.

'Have you eaten today?' she asked abruptly.

'A coffee and a chocolate biscuit while I waited for

Mike to audition,' Claire admitted. 'I felt too upset to manage anything more substantial.'

Lynn sighed and raised her eyes heavenward. 'I guessed that would be the case, and I don't suppose you ate anything for breakfast either?'

'Not much,' Claire admitted. 'I felt too nervous.' She never wanted to eat before an audition, her stomach always tied itself into so many knots even the thought of food made her feel ill.

'Oh Claire, you really are the limit!' Her friend sighed now and then she smiled, 'Fortunately I was offered another assignment today so I went to the delicatessen and bought a couple of pizzas and a bottle of cheap plonk.' She rose to her feet. 'So you stay where you are and dry your hair and I'll go and put the finishing touches to the meal.'

When Claire walked into the kitchen fifteen minutes later she realised that Lynn had indeed made a special effort. There was even a vase of freesias on the table, their perfume vying with the tempting aroma of cheese and herbs wafting from the oven. Lynn's thoughtful gesture brought the tears to Claire's eyes. Jake Svenson's contemptuous attitude had upset her more than she liked to admit. It had hurt! She would have liked an opportunity to show him he was mistaken about her, if only to prove him wrong. He was an arrogant devil! It would do him a world of good to have to admit a mistake for once.

She walked forward, pulling out a chair as Lynn gestured for her to sit at the table. 'I feel such a fraud,' she said. 'You shouldn't be looking after me like this. You're the one who earned her living today. I only succeeded in making a mess of everything.'

'Don't be an idiot, Claire! It was just one of those things.'

'Yes, I would agree with you there.' Claire's expression was rueful. 'And the thing's name was Alan Crosby!'

Lynn was crouching in front of the open oven and

she turned a flushed face in Claire's direction. 'Oh no! I might have guessed! What did he do? Instigate a full-scale row?'

Claire nodded unhappily and began to tell Lynn the full story. 'And prepare yourself for a further shock,' she finished gloomily. 'The man who came through the door was none other than Jake Svenson.'

Lynn sighed in mock anguish and put the pizzas she was carrying on to the hot plates she had prepared for them earlier. 'Oh Claire, it could only happen to you!'

'I know it,' Claire agreed with a wry grimace. 'I hated him on sight and I'm afraid I was awfully rude to him. He was so arrogant and self-righteous, my only thought was to show him that he couldn't intimidate me. Perhaps if I'd been more conciliatory he might have overlooked everything else, but he made me so angry that I just blurted out the first outrageous remarks that came into my head.'

'Oh Claire, that temper!'

'Yes, I know,' Claire sighed. 'I could have kicked myself once I'd calmed down a bit. I ought to have crawled to the arrogant beast, done anything I could to persuade him to offer me the part.' She suspected that Jake Svenson would be used to people hanging on to his every word. Her attitude must have been a terrific shock to him.

'Don't look so fierce, love,' Lynn said now. 'If he was as unpleasant as you say, I don't suppose you could have done anything to change his mind.' Lynn paused a moment and took a sip of wine before adding, 'I must say he came over rather well on the television, utterly charming. Although I remember thinking at the time that he looked as though he could be ruthless, given the opportunity. That was half his charm, I daresay. Powerful men are nearly always fascinating.'

Privately Claire was inclined to agree. She had thought him the rudest, most arrogant man she had ever met but that hadn't stopped her recognising his attraction, and the knowledge didn't help her mood one bit. 'Oh, I've no doubt he can turn on the charm when he wants to,' she put in crossly, sawing at her pizza with unnecessarily violent strokes. 'And he certainly knew what a winner he was.'

'And what about Mike's audition? How did it go?' Lynn asked now.

Claire brightened visibly. 'The one cheerful spot in the awful day. Mike was offered the part of one of the wreckers.' She took another gulp of wine before adding. 'He's ideal, of course. Small and dark and very Celtic-looking.'

'Joan will be pleased.'

'Yes,' Claire agreed. 'She never seems to begrudge working all day to support them both but it must be irritating at times.' She pushed away her plate with a sigh of pleasure. 'That was delicious, Lynn. I feel much more cheerful now.' She leaned forward, her elbows on the worktop. 'But that's enough about the audition for now. Tell me about your assignment today. It must have gone well if you've been offered extra work?'

'Yes, it did . . .'

The telephone rang shrilly, interrupting Lynn's explanation and she sighed as she pushed herself to her feet. 'No you sit there and finish your coffee,' she said as Claire began to get up as well. 'I'll answer that.'

Claire sipped her coffee slowly, turning her head in surprise as Lynn returned after a few seconds.

'It's your agent,' Lynn explained quickly, a kindling excitement in her eyes. 'You don't think . . .?'

Claire shook her head dismissively as she pushed herself to her feet, but even so she couldn't prevent a faint surge of excitement as she picked up the receiver and held it to her ear.

'Claire Grant,' she stated abruptly, her usually clear tones husky with tension. There was a momentary silence as she listened to the voice on the other end of the line but then she gave a gasp of shock. 'I don't believe it!' she exclaimed. 'Are you sure it's not a joke?' Silence for a moment and then: 'But why? They never hinted . . .'

Claire turned towards her friend and mouthed: 'Marvellous news!' Before returning her attention to the telephone. 'Repeat that figure will you,' Lynn heard her say. 'Yes, yes, I agree! It is!' She nodded her head rapidly. 'Tomorrow at eleven,' she added. 'Of course I'll be there.' And after a moment. 'Lunch? Yes, yes, if you like! Goodbye for now!'

Claire dropped the receiver with a clatter on to the cradle and turned to face Lynn, pressing her shaking hands to her flushed cheeks. 'You're not going to believe this. I don't think I quite believe it myself.'

'Calm down and tell me what he said,' Lynn commanded.

'Dave Tillson, the assistant director, rang my agent about ten minutes ago.' She turned bemused green eyes on her friend. 'They've offered me a part in the film after all.'

Lynn rushed towards her and hugged her. 'That's wonderful news, Claire. I'm so pleased for you.'

'It's even more wonderful than you think. Lord! I shall have to sit down. I feel positively shaky.' She made her way to the nearest chair and collapsed weakly into it and Lynn stood and watched her, amusement vying with curiosity on her beautiful features.

'Come on, Claire, spill the beans. I'm dying with curiosity.'

'They've offered me the part of Désirée and it's one of the main supporting roles. The actress who was to play her has just discovered she's pregnant. I did read the part but I never dreamed . . .' She broke off and shook her head. 'For one thing my accent was appalling and I was sure that Jake Svenson would never let me within a mile of his precious film.' She turned to Lynn, anxiety already beginning to dim her earlier excitement. 'How am I going to work with that man after today? He must hate the sight of me.'

'Calm down, Claire. You've no right to be worrying about anything at this moment in time. After all he has offered you a job. Believe me he's not going to deliberately antagonise you once you are on the set. Too much hangs in the balance. Think of the good things,' she urged. 'Think of the money.'

'Gosh yes,' Claire's face cleared and she gave an almost ecstatic sigh. 'Just wait until you hear how much they're going to pay me. No wonder my agent has invited me to lunch tomorrow. We shan't need to worry about the rent for months after this.'

Claire clutched at the side of Mike's car and clung on for grim death. Until they had turned off on to the narrow roadway leading to Ardwennan Manor she had been more than happy to feast her eyes on the stunning scenery surrounding them but now she sat with her eyes fixed rigidly ahead, her knuckles showing white where they gripped the car door. Mike, however, was apparently oblivious to their hair-raising situation and he turned a cheerful face towards her.

'They didn't exaggerate, did they?' He grinned. 'I'm glad I don't have to negotiate these bends in the depths of winter.'

Claire tried to smile back but it was impossible. 'Please watch the road, Mike,' she begged as calmly as she could. She risked one brief glance over Mike's shoulder, shivered and turned her face away again quickly. 'I've no desire to end my promising career smashed to pieces on those rocks.'

'Hey, you really don't like this, do you? Sorry, love.' Mike was instantly contrite. 'We're quite safe, actually. The road has been cambered pretty efficiently.'

Claire shivered again. 'I'm terrified of heights actually,' she admitted. 'It's perfectly stupid, I know, but I'm the type who feels dizzy on the top deck of a bus.'

Mike laughed but then sobered quickly. 'Hell, Claire! You have read the script, I suppose?'

Claire turned her head and nodded. 'Don't worry, Mike. I do realise that I have to do an awful lot of clambering around on cliff edges. I shall get used to it.' She gritted her teeth. 'I shall have to get used to it!

There's no way I'm going to lose this chance to advance my career, just because of some stupid phobia. And once I'm into the part I shall become so absorbed that I shall forget my fears.'

Mike agreed quietly. He was too kind a person to say that he thought it highly unlikely that her fears would disappear so conveniently, but he was not required to say anything further because at that moment they rounded a bend in the road and came in sight of Ardwennan Manor, the location for *Wrecker's Bride*. For the last few hundred yards the road had left the precipitous cliff edge and their view had been restricted by high banks on either side, but now it shot out into the open again. The view was breathtaking. Claire let out her breath in an audible gasp and Mike stopped the car immediately, reaching into the back for his camera before leaping out, jumping the ditch at the side of the road and scrambling up the hillside to the best vantage point.

Claire was content to remain exactly where she was, simply drinking in the view. Ardwennan Manor was perfect. With the late afternoon sunshine glinting on its mullioned windows it looked so beautiful as to appear unreal. It was exactly the right setting for the film, of course. Perched as it was on the very edge of the cliff top. Its weathered stone looking as much a part of the landscape as the jagged rocks, breasting the foaming water below the house.

Apparently the owners had been happy to lease the house to the film company and were currently spending the proceeds on an extended trip to the States. Claire wondered how they could bear to leave such a beautiful place, knowing it would be used as a film set. Not only that, but some of the cast and crew were to be housed in the Manor. The domestic staff were staying, of course. Along with extra help hired by the film company. But even so the ancient building would be subject to a fair amount of wear and tear over the next few months.

The door of the small car jerked open suddenly and Claire turned to smile at Mike as he levered his wiry frame behind the wheel, raking his fingers through his dark hair in an attempt to restore it to some sort of order. He turned to Claire, his eyes alight with excitement.

'This place is fantastic! Really fantastic! I couldn't have chosen better myself. Svenson certainly knows what he's doing. It seems almost an intrusion driving up to the Manor in this car. I feel we ought to be driving a coach and four and wearing crinolines and . . .'

Claire interrupted him with a grin. 'I agree, you would look just great in a crinoline! But seriously, love, you're in the wrong century.' She laughed as he pulled a face at her. 'But I do see what you mean. The Manor belongs so exactly to the period of the script that it's almost eerie.'

'I only hope that it's more comfortable inside than it looks from here,' Mike replied cheerfully, pushing the car into gear, so that they began to move slowly down the road.

Claire shivered suddenly. She had been given a room in the manor house itself but Mike was to stay in the village hotel. It was a far from ideal situation and she couldn't help worrying about it. 'Don't talk about it, Mike,' she said now. 'I wish to goodness I wasn't staying there. You're the only person I know.'

'You're not still fretting about that, are you?' Mike's tone was deliberately bracing. 'Honestly Claire, you've no need to worry, practically everyone will be friendly.'

'I noticed you qualified that statement,' Claire replied with a faint worried grimace. 'Jake Svenson doesn't like me, you know that. He's obviously not going to smooth my path. I'm beginning to wonder if everyone will follow his lead and I shall be totally isolated.'

'Of course you won't,' Mike scoffed as he swung the car around yet another tight bend, the wheels narrowly missing the ditch at one side of the road. He shot her an amused glance, his dark eyes lingering for a moment on her glowing features. 'There's no way a houseful of men are going to ignore you and Svenson's main concern is going to be the film, not you.'

Claire relaxed slightly. Even though Mike didn't know the full story of her disagreement with the director his words were reassuring. 'You're very good for my ego, Mike.' She paused, pulling a small face. 'But even you can't reconcile me to more than three months on location with Marianne Lejeune. By all accounts she hates women anyway and if rumour is true and she and Jake Svenson are lovers, she's bound to be unpleasant to me.'

'She's a bitch,' Mike agreed bluntly. 'But she is a professional down to her fingertips. Keep your eyes off the director and I should think she will leave you completely alone.'

Claire shivered, a sudden mental image of cold blue eyes set in a hard, unforgiving countenance flickering into her brain. That was one piece of advice that she was not going to ignore. Jake Svenson was dangerous and she was going to stay as far out of his orbit as it was possible to be.

Mike was grinning as he added, 'You may be too high on the credits to bed down with *hoi polloi* at the local inn, but believe me, you'll be way below our fair Marianne's touch.' He smiled again reassuringly and patted Claire's arm. 'You'll be fine. It's all good experience and when you're a star with your name in lights you'll look back and wonder what all the fuss was about.'

Claire tried to remember Mike's reassuring words later that evening as she stood in the drawing room, a glass of sherry clutched in one faintly trembling hand, but it was a hopeless task. She was terrified of meeting Jake Svenson again and it seemed as though nothing could change that emotion. She had dressed with particular care, her make-up discreet and understated, her soft green woollen dress demure and high-necked, everything

designed to play down the image which she felt sure the
director must carry in his brain. But even so her self-
confidence was at a very low ebb.

She could see Jake Svenson now, across the other
side of the room, his dark head bent as he listened
attentively to what Penny Allinson, the art director, was
telling him. His tall figure was difficult to miss. Even in
tonight's distinguished company he seemed to dominate
the occasion, his black dinner jacket fitting like a
second skin over his broad shoulders, the harsh planes
of his face softening as he smiled at something Penny
said to him.

And Claire was compelled to admit that the woman
standing by his side was equally as eye-catching. Claire
had seen Marianne Lejeune in photographs and on film
many times, but she was still unprepared for the full
impact of her beauty in the flesh. She was perfection
from the top of her shining blonde head to the tip of
her ridiculously high-heeled sandals.

Dave Tillson was standing beside Claire and had
obviously been following the direction of her gaze,
because he spoke now, breaking into her thoughts.
'Marianne only arrived an hour ago,' he murmured.
'She's been travelling most of the day and Jake was
afraid she wouldn't make it. *Dark Lady* finished way
behind schedule. I hope to God she's not completely
exhausted.'

She didn't look exhausted, Claire thought. On the
contrary, her beautiful face glowed with health and
vivacity. She was hanging on to the director's arm and
smiling up into his face as though she would like to eat
him alive. For some reason Claire found it a disturbing
sight and she turned back to Dave, an expression of
half-comical dismay on her beautiful face. 'Can you tell
me just exactly what I'm doing here among all these
people?' Her gaze flickered around the room once again
and she shook her head, bronze curls feathering softly
across her cheeks. 'I must have been mad to take the
part. I don't know the first thing about film making!'

She hadn't intended to voice her insecurities but today her confidence was at rock bottom. She felt gauche and inexperienced and it didn't help that almost everyone else in the room was wildly talented. She knew she was lucky. Her role as Désirée was a fantastic opportunity but she had a niggling feeling that Jake Svenson would be the first to cheer if she made a hash of it, and the thought did nothing to boost her ego.

Dave had listened quietly to her outburst, and now he smiled, his brown eyes kind, reminding Claire more than ever of the rather well-worn teddy bear she'd had as a child, his thinning brown hair sticking out in tufts all around his face.

'You're here because you have talent, Claire,' he insisted. 'And you're more than capable of playing the role of Désirée.' He smiled again. 'I auditioned you, remember. I know exactly what kind of work you're capable of producing and you wouldn't be here if I didn't believe in you. I do realise that you're bound to be nervous but please, let's not have any more nonsense!'

Claire couldn't help responding to the warmth of his manner with a smile. Even though she was far from being reassured his friendliness was balm to her shattered nerves. He was genuinely sympathetic, seeming to understand exactly what she was feeling. 'You're being very kind to me, Dave,' she murmured gratefully. In fact she would have been lost without him this evening. He'd met her, hesitating nervously outside the drawing room and taken her under his wing immediately. It was impossible not to like him. He'd been kind and helpful, the complete opposite to Jake Svenson who had ignored her pointedly all evening. She had told herself that Dave's friendship more than compensated for the director's unpleasant attitude but the words sounded weak and unconvincing to her own ears. Dave was still talking but Claire swilled the sherry around in her glass and watched it gloomily, giving him only half her attention.

'I'm not being kind, Claire. I promise you I mean everything I say. You are both talented and beautiful and believe me, you're going to be a very big success.'

'Dave darling, flirting again? Whatever would Myra have to say?' The words were murmured in a quiet, lightly mocking voice which brought a wave of dark red colour to Dave's pleasant face. Marianne Lejeune's arrival had gone unnoticed until then but at last Claire's attention was fully engaged. Marianne was even more beautiful at close quarters, her pale skin and delicate profile absolutely flawless, but even so it was on the man standing by her side that Claire's eyes automatically fastened, the colour surging into her cheeks as she caught his eye.

She didn't need to be a mind reader to recognise Jake Svenson's thoughts. They were written in letters ten feet high all over his uncompromising features. His opinion of her hadn't changed at all since they'd last met, Claire realised unhappily. Far from it! He had heard Dave's kind attempts at reassurance and like Marianne Lejeune put the worst possible construction on his words.

Was it always to be like this? Was she always going to appear to this man in the very worst possible light? Claire wondered, continuing to stare at him helplessly, her green eyes huge and vulnerable, reflecting the confused state of her emotions. He stared back coldly, seeming to tower over her, dark and dangerous, disrupting her senses. Claire wanted to look away but their eyes were locked together, the silence lengthening, tension mounting until Claire could almost feel it hammering against her skull. And he felt it too, Claire realised, his eyes narrowing, their colour darkening to a deep slate blue, some indefinable emotion stirring briefly in their depths, taking Claire's breath away, leaving her weak and trembling and trying very hard to fight it.

And then, just as suddenly it was gone. Her gaze was free and the director was staring at her as though she was the most loathsome object he had ever seen, or so it seemed to Claire. She dropped her betraying eyes, her sherry glass trembling between her fingers. She still wasn't quite sure what had happened to her, but it had been one heck of an experience, and one she was in no hurry to repeat.

'Miss Grant's still stunned by your eloquence, Dave.' The light laugh which accompanied Marianne's words grated on Claire's oversensitive nerves. She would have liked to have turned her back and walked out of the room leaving all her disturbing emotions behind, but she simply hadn't the courage, nor was she even certain that her wobbly legs would support her.

'Claire understands me.' Dave's voice was gruff but the smile he sent Claire was as warm as ever and her own lips tilted tremulously in return. 'She was feeling a little overawed by us all,' he explained. 'I was just telling her that she had nothing to worry about.'

'Darling, as Dave says you mustn't worry.' Marianne was smiling at Claire in apparent friendliness with perhaps just a taint of condescension in her honeyed tones. 'We're not ogres you know. We shall all help you as much as we can.'

Claire squirmed inwardly. Looking at Jake Svenson's shuttered face she knew that he at least wouldn't be offering her help of any sort.

Marianne was still holding the stage and she half-turned, her beautiful smile embracing Jake Svenson possessively. 'Jake was assistant director on my very first film. Do you remember what a hash I made of it, darling? I was almost in despair.'

'I'm sorry, Marianne, my memory would appear to be at fault.' Jake was smiling into Marianne's face, his blue eyes as warm and caressing as his husky voice. 'I can only recollect a beautiful and extremely talented actress, word perfect for every scene.'

Claire felt sick. It was outrageous flattery but Marianne lapped it up, her laugh rippling gently. 'Jake, you flatterer.' She laughed again. 'I like it.' Her arm looped confidingly into his. 'Now I'm sure Dave and

Miss Grant will excuse us if we move on. We want to have a word with one or two other people before dinner.' She smiled at Claire. 'We'll have another chat later, my dear. And if you have any more worries, please feel free to come and discuss them with me at any time.'

Claire smiled weakly back and watched as Marianne and Jake walked across the room towards Richard Angrams, the leading man. There had been no word of farewell for her from the director. He had ignored her completely, and it hurt. Maybe as Dave said, she was right for the part of Désirée. Maybe she would even prove to be a success, but it seemed that in Jake Svenson's eyes she was stuck for ever with her image as a good time girl and nothing would change that.

They went into dinner shortly afterwards. The dining room was beautiful. Even in her present miserable state Claire couldn't help but notice. She sat obediently on the chair which Dave held out for her and allowed her glance to flicker around the room. The huge, polished refectory table sparkled with cut glass and silver, snowy white linen napkins lying beside every plate. The softly shadowed wall lights were switched on but the table itself was illuminated by tall, white, sweetly scented candles in silver holders, the portraits on the walls gazing down with evident approval on the distinguished company in its beautiful setting.

Claire was impressed, but it didn't improve her mood. She ate and drank what was set before her without tasting it. Dave Tillson and her neighbour on the other side, an extremely youthful looking cameraman, talked, she laughed and smiled and answered when she had to, but her mind was far away. Without even moving her head she could see the director at the head of the table and time and again her eyes turned that way, as though they were on strings and he was working the controls.

And she saw a different man from the individual he showed to her. His lean body relaxed, a smile hovering around his well-shaped mouth as he divided his attention equally between Marianne and the art director on his other side. He laughed suddenly, showing even white teeth and Claire turned away abruptly, taking a large swig of the red wine which had replaced the white in her glass, enjoying the sensation as it ran down her throat, moistening her dry mouth, warming the chill which seemed to have crept into her stomach.

Her eyes slid to the head of the table yet again. He looked so pleased with himself, she thought crossly, surrounded by admiring women. He knew exactly what effect he was having on them and as far as Claire could see he was encouraging it. But of course he was a man. It was okay for him to behave in that way, but let a woman do the same and he was soon looking down his high-bridged nose at them. Maybe it was Dutch courage but Claire was beginning to feel quite angry. He didn't like her. So, what the hell! Everyone else had been very kind. Who needed Jake Svenson?

Dave had been talking to her all evening, telling her about his family and at last she began to listen. Clearly he adored both his wife and children. So much for your nasty suspicious mind, Jake Svenson, Claire's green eyes sparkled, betraying her angry thoughts and Dave saw her face and misinterpreted, his own expression rueful as he said: 'I'm sorry, Claire. Am I boring you? Once I start on the story of my life I tend to get carried away.'

'Don't be silly.' Claire's response was immediate and contrite. 'I'm not bored, far from it.' She smiled warmly to emphasise her words. It wasn't Dave's fault that Jake Svenson was such a pig. She had no right to make him the whipping boy for her own insecurities. 'I enjoy listening to you,' she added sincerely. 'Please don't stop now.'

This time she gave him all her attention, her green eyes fixed with flattering interest on his flushed face. She was still aware of the director's tall figure at the head of the table. She could almost feel his eyes

crawling down her spine, but she turned her back
deliberately, determined to block him out of her mind.

Maybe it was the wine, or Dave's undemanding
company, but gradually she began to relax too. She
found herself opening up, telling him about her family
and her life in London. Dave was in a mellow mood.
He relaxed in his seat, listened and smiled, his plump
face perspiring gently, and gradually the whole story of
her disagreement with Jake Svenson came filtering out.

'What can I do, Dave?' she asked when she had told
him everything. 'I know my behaviour was appalling
but he was so damned arrogant and sure of himself and
I was already in a fury with Alan, I couldn't control my
temper.' She shrugged, watching his face. She didn't
really believe that he would be able to help her, but it
had relieved her mind, just telling him.

Dave sighed now, leaning forward in his seat, one
elbow propped on the table. 'You want my advice,
Claire and for what it's worth you've got it.' He paused,
his plump face serious for once. 'You must explain to
Jake this evening, tell him the truth and apologise. He's
a reasonable man. He will at least give you a fair
hearing.' Claire was inclined to doubt that and it took
Dave a few minutes to convince her. 'What have you
got to lose?' he asked at last. 'How will he ever discover
the truth unless you explain it to him?'

Yes, thought Claire gazing down the table, but can I
do it?

CHAPTER FOUR

It had been amazingly difficult to get Jake Svenson alone, Claire reflected later that evening, an almost impossible task. Marianne had clung to his side like glue and everyone on the cast seemed to have a problem which they couldn't wait to discuss with him. They had returned to the drawing room for coffee and he had taken up position immediately beside the huge stone fireplace, one long arm propped against the mantle, his linen very white against the pale tan of his skin.

They had crowded around him, drawn like bees to nectar and she had watched him helplessly from across the room, unwilling to push her way through the crowd to attract his attention, half-hoping that he would be occupied all evening so that she would have an excuse not to speak to him. She was ashamed to feel her body trembling. She was nervous, scared to death, cursing herself silently for allowing Dave to talk her into this.

But she had cornered him at last and now her worst fears were realised. He listened in complete, nerve-racking silence as she told her story, those cold, blue eyes seeming to pierce her skull and read the words in her brain before she spoke them. Claire fell silent at last, her whole body stiff with tension. She had finished her explanation and she could see on his face that he didn't believe a word, his lips curved into something very like a sneer.

'You don't believe me!' The words were hoarse, torn out of Claire's dry throat. She wanted to cry, or shout and throw things. It had taken all her courage to face him this evening and now she felt as though he'd just kicked her in the teeth.

He was still watching her, blue eyes glazed with ice. 'Did you really expect me to do so?' It was a rhetorical question, but Claire couldn't have forced out a reply even if he'd wanted her to. 'You're no fool, Miss Grant.' His blue eyes ran over her, telling her without words exactly what he did think she was. 'You appear to have Dave wrapped around your little finger. Let that be enough for you. And don't worry,' he paused, taking a sip of the brandy in his glass, watching her coolly over the rim, 'providing you work hard and do the job you're paid to do, I shan't give you a hard time.'

Claire could feel her temper building, like a volcano ready to explode. She felt her chin go up and she knew her anger was showing in the bright sparkle of her green eyes. 'That's very generous of you,' she murmured in sweetly barbed tones.

He raised his glass, his smile frankly mocking. 'I'm renowned for my generous impulses.'

Claire simmered. 'It wouldn't matter what I said to you, would it? I could have a dozen witnesses to confirm my side of the story and you still wouldn't believe me.' He raised one dark brow, silently acknowledging the truth of her words and Claire felt an almost primitive urge to lash out, wipe that superior mocking smile from his handsome face. She took a deep breath, clenching her hands tightly by her side, resisting temptation. 'What's the use,' she sighed angrily. 'You're never going to give me the benefit of the doubt.'

The dark brows rose to new heights. 'Doubt, Miss Grant, what possible doubt could I have? As I remember you condemned yourself out of your own mouth. Now if you'll excuse me . . .' He turned and with a faint inclination of his dark head moved to place his empty glass on the table at one side.

He was going, Claire realised. Dismissing her as though she was an irritating child. Her explanations and apologies ignored. Instinctively her fingers reached out, clutching his dark sleeve. She wouldn't let him do this to her. She had to make him listen. 'Don't go! Not yet! Please!' she begged.

He paused, his blue eyes very sharp and Claire saw

that for the first time that evening she had managed to pierce his cold shell. He was annoyed, clearly not used to people who didn't take their dismissal with a good grace. She felt just like an irritating wasp, buzzing around Jake Svenson's head. She was a nuisance and any minute now he was going to reach out and swat her senseless. She stared at him, hopelessly out of her depth. She ought to have let him leave as he'd intended, she couldn't think, never mind speak with him watching her so intently.

'Please Mr Svenson I ...' She bit her lip, gazing at her hands. She mustn't let him affect her like this, he would think she was a fool as well as everything else. She took a deep breath and tried again. 'You've made a mistake. Surely, you must see, if I was the sort of girl you suspect, I wouldn't care a damn what you thought of me. I'd just go right on behaving exactly as I pleased.'

His eyes narrowed. 'Maybe,' he murmured, conceding a point. 'But I am the director of this film. You know that now; you didn't know at the audition.'

Claire heard herself sighing. She would have liked to have rushed into angry speech, denying his words, but they had touched a tender spot. Would she have behaved as badly if she'd realised he was the director? She didn't know and the thought threw her completely. She bent her head, soft hair falling around her face. 'That's true,' she agreed reluctantly, gnawing at her bottom lip, feeling foolish.

'Stumped at last, Miss Grant?' His voice was deceptively gentle and Claire's head shot up. He was watching her, blue eyes gleaming, his lips curved into a gently mocking smile. 'Don't disappoint me,' he added softly. 'I feel sure it's not like you to abandon the race at the first hurdle.'

Claire's chin was up, her green eyes flashing. 'I realise I'm fair game this evening, Mr Svenson, but next time pick on someone your own size. You're baiting me deliberately, knowing I can't answer back.' Anger was

Claire's only defence. One small, frankly mocking smile from him and she'd turned to jelly, her heart drumming so fast she could hardly breathe.

She swung round abruptly, intending to make her escape, but he caught her arm with his fingers, holding her back. 'That was unfair,' he murmured. 'My apologies.' He was watching her, his blue eyes intent and Claire stood and trembled in silence, breathing hard. 'I don't know whether you're telling the truth or not,' he stated quietly. 'But I do know that if we continue to indulge in a running battle it could kill this film, and at this moment *Wrecker's Bride* is my only concern.' He held out his hand. 'I propose a truce, at least until the film is finished.'

What could Claire do? She had hoped for more, much more. She had wanted him to believe her, as Dave had done. She had hoped for his trust, and yet realised that she'd done nothing to deserve it. She took a deep breath and put her hand into his, returning the cool, hard clasp of his fingers, trying hard not to let her own hand tremble. He was giving her a chance. It was more than she had expected at this time yesterday. It would have to be enough!

Claire slept badly that night. The bed was unfamiliar and she couldn't relax, too many things had happened, so she tossed and turned far into the night, waking early, roused by the dawn chorus, crawling out of bed at last, dazed and heavy eyed. But it was a beautiful morning. The moment she pulled back the flowered curtains she felt her spirits beginning to rise. The sun was shining, the sea beyond the headland a deep, translucent blue.

Suddenly she was bursting with enthusiasm, yester-day's doubts and fears illusory things. She remembered her conversation with the director and she was filled with hope. He had proposed a truce. Maybe it wasn't quite the open-hearted welcome she had hoped for, but it was a start, and she could build on it.

She dressed quickly in jeans and sweater, whipping

through her usual morning routine at top speed so that she reached the dining room long before anyone else and had to eat alone. She wandered over to the window with her coffee cup when she'd finished her toast, feasting her eyes on the view, blue sea and in the distance a long, yellow stretch of sand. It looked very tempting. The sea the same vivid colour that Claire had encountered in the Mediterranean last summer.

She finished her coffee and wandered out of the dining room at last, turning right along the passage, intending to take a circuitous route back to her bedroom. She was longing to explore. Old houses were fascinating, full of tiny staircases and odd little rooms and last night she'd been far too preoccupied to take very much notice of her surroundings. She walked on, her high heels echoing on the worn stone, her head turning from side to side, absorbing everything of interest that she passed.

The panelled corridors seemed to go on for ever but at last she strolled into the main entrance hall, her steps slowing of their own accord, as she gazed around, stunned by the magnificence of her surroundings.

Her streamlined, utterly practical bedroom had been a disappointment to Claire, but there was no trace of the twentieth century here; the hall had sprung straight out of the past. The crystal chandeliers were fuelled by electricity of course and when she looked carefully she could see the switches set discreetly into the wooden panelled walls, but otherwise the portraits gazed down on a scene which must have changed little over the centuries.

Claire moved slowly forwards, her fingers trailing over the banister, enjoying the silky, sensuous feel of the wood beneath her hands. She gazed upwards. It was a magnificent staircase, its balustrade supported by knots of carved fruit and curving wreaths of wooden flowers. Everywhere she looked there were beautiful things which had been loved and cherished down through the years. It gave her a good feeling and a smile curved her generous mouth as she moved to stand on tip toe in front of the huge, stone hearth, drawn by the gilt-framed portrait above it.

The painting was of a man in uniform, not a handsome figure, but there was something about the warm grey eyes which drew her attention and held it. 'Lord St Avon,' she murmured quietly, reading the inscription at the bottom of the frame. 'Killed in action aboard the *Pegasus*.'

'During the Napoleonic Wars, so they tell me.'

Claire's head swivelled, her eyes wide and shocked. The words had echoed her own thoughts almost exactly, but it was the deep, slightly husky tones in which they were spoken that brought the flush to her cheeks and set her heart pounding a wild tattoo in her breast. She stared at Jake Svenson in consternation, wondering why her body always reacted so violently to his presence, wishing desperately that it wouldn't.

He strolled slowly forward now, his hands thrust deep into the pockets of his jacket. 'What's the matter, Miss Grant? Seen a ghost?' he murmured, arching one faintly mocking brow. 'Or has the cat got your tongue?'

Claire didn't know whether he was deliberately baiting her or not, but she did know that those intensely blue eyes saw too much and where he was concerned she had far too much to hide. 'You gave me a shock,' she replied with as much composure as she could muster. 'I was just wondering in which battle Lord St Avon was killed and then you spoke. It was unnerving that's all.' Her voice was faintly husky but she was proud that she had her jumping nerves under control.

He bent his head back now, revealing the firm brown column of his throat, his blue eyes on the portrait and Claire used that moment to stare quite openly at him. In a pair of tight blue jeans, a faded denim jacket stretched tautly over his broad shoulders, he made compulsive viewing. He was a magnificent male animal. Claire didn't want to see his attraction but she just couldn't help herself.

He turned and she dropped her eyes instantly, apparently completely absorbed by the worn grey stones at her feet. 'And did you reach any conclusion, Miss Grant?' he murmured gently. Claire raised her head, her cheeks pink, bewilderment on her face. 'About Lord St Avon and his final battle? You say you were just thinking about it when I spoke.'

He was still watching her and Claire could see from his face that he didn't expect an answer. He thought she'd been pretending an interest she didn't really feel and now he was deliberately setting her up. If this was his idea of a truce, Claire decided that she didn't appreciate it. 'From the date I would say that he died during the Battle of the Nile,' Claire replied coolly.

His eyes widened and he nodded abruptly and Claire felt a spurt of pleasure because she'd been able to disconcert him so easily. 'Right first time, Miss Grant.' His eyes flicked over her. 'Brains as well as beauty. You surprise me. I wouldn't have thought that history was your scene.'

Maybe Claire was being oversensitive but she read insult into every word of that little speech. 'It isn't my scene, as you call it.' There was a cold snap in her tones which she made no attempt to hide. 'In fact I'm abysmally ignorant about history in general and the Napoleonic Wars in particular. It was a lucky guess on my part.' She paused, her green eyes flashing angrily 'I'm sure that makes you feel a whole lot better. Now if you'll excuse me, I have things to do.'

She turned around with an angry jerk, but as he had done once before he put out a hand and stopped her, his fingers curling like a vice around her wrist.

'Let me go!' she snapped.

But he shook his head. 'No, wait a minute. I want to apologise.'

Claire's whole body was stiff with outrage. 'I seem to have heard all this before. You apologise far too easily, Mr Svenson. I don't believe it means a thing to you.'

'Point taken, Miss Grant.' He was still holding tightly

to her wrist and although Claire tried again to pull away, he wouldn't let her.

'Let me go,' she said, but this time her words lacked conviction. He was smiling down at her with great charm and a strange trembling sensation had invaded the pit of Claire's stomach.

'I don't blame you for wanting to snap my head off,' he murmured with disarming candour. 'I realise I wasn't exactly tactful. I have a careless tongue and one hell of a big mouth sometimes, but believe me, I didn't intend to upset you.'

Behind her Claire heard a door open and close again, but she didn't turn her head, she was frozen to the spot, her eyes glued to the director.

'Does the truce still hold?' He smiled again, making Claire's heart skid crazily in her breast. 'Or am I still in the dog house?'

Claire wanted to be angry but she just couldn't resist that smile and she could feel her own lips curving in response to it. 'Maybe I was being oversensitive,' she murmured.

'You were expecting the worst,' Jake agreed quietly.

That was true enough, Claire reflected silently. She found this new, smiling Jake Svenson pretty hard to believe. She couldn't hope that he'd changed his mind about her so quickly. It must all be an act, but act or not, she knew she didn't want it to end. 'I'm sorry,' she nodded, 'perhaps that's true.'

He was still smiling down at her. 'Will you allow me to make amends for upsetting you?' he asked quietly. He lifted his wrist and glanced quickly at his watch. 'You're obviously interested in the manor house, perhaps you would allow me to give you a guided tour?' He raised one dark brow in silent question and Claire could feel the hot, betraying colour flooding her cheeks. If only for the sake of her pride Claire knew she ought at least to hesitate but it was with no real sense of shock that she heard herself saying:

'I'd like to look around. It's very kind of you to offer.'

'Right,' he smiled, 'fine, where shall we start? Do you have any preferences?' He actually seemed pleased that Claire had accepted his offer, but she still couldn't take his changed manner at face value. She kept looking at him as they walked around, wondering what was going on in his head, but gradually she relaxed. The house was beautiful and the director's husky voice had an almost hypnotic effect on her nerves so that by the end of the tour she had become completely fascinated, drawn as much by the play of emotion on his face as by the antique furniture and paintings on display in the old house.

At last they stopped outside his study. He had given her far more time than she expected but he still seemed in no hurry. He stretched lazily, one long arm propped against the door frame and looked down at Claire with a warm, heart-stopping smile. 'Have I bored you silly?' he asked.

Claire shook her head, trying desperately not to show how it disturbed her, standing here with him like this. 'I enjoyed it,' she murmured. That was the understatement of the year, she realised. She had been able to feel the old image of Jake Svenson dissolving out of her brain. Today there was charm and humour behind the blue eyes. She knew, who better, that they could blaze with anger, but the new image was so strong that she could barely remember that other, harsher aspect of his personality.

'You made it very interesting,' she added sincerely. 'It would be frustrating staying in a house like this, not knowing the first thing about its history. I did borrow some books about Cornwall from the library before we came, but there wasn't a word about Ardwennan Manor in them.' She stopped and bit her lip. She was talking too much, but she couldn't just stand there in silence, not with him watching her so intently.

'I have a couple of books about the area in the study,' he said now. 'Would you like to come in and have a look at them?'

'I couldn't put you to the trouble.' Claire's voice shook. If she hadn't known better she would have said that he wanted to spend time with her.

'No trouble,' he brushed her half-hearted protest to one side, levering himself from the wall in one fluid movement. 'Come in for a moment. I should be able to find them quite easily.'

He held the door open so that Claire could precede him into the room, standing so close that her arm brushed his chest as she passed him. She welcomed that touch. She knew she was a fool. He was dangerously attractive when he was in this mood. She ought to back away now while she still had the chance.

She hovered just inside the door watching with disturbed eyes as he searched through the drawers of the huge desk, dominating one corner of the room. The sun was slanting in gold bars through the mullions, catching his dark head, tipping his hair with silver gilt. Her eyes followed the bar of light as it picked out the heavy leather chairs and the jewelled brightness of the polished floor, but inevitably her gaze was drawn back towards the director. Why was he being so kind to her? She couldn't understand it. Her mind was going round and round, exploring the same old question, like a record stuck in a well-worn groove and she was still no nearer to finding an answer.

At last the director raised his head, satisfaction in his voice as he handed the leather volumes across the desk towards Claire. 'Here they are. Try them and see what you think. They were both written by local vicars. I found them heavy going in places.' He smiled. 'But you can always skip the bits that don't interest you.'

Claire was forced to leave her place by the door and walk across the room on shaky legs, towards him. 'Thank you.' She took the books, careful not to let their fingers touch. 'I'll let you have them back as soon as I can.'

'Take your time.' He pulled a small face. 'I suspect I shall be far too busy over the next couple of months to need them myself.' He walked around the desk, propping his lean frame against one polished corner, looking as though he was settled for the day. 'Sometimes I think I must be out of my mind, staying in this profession,' he smiled, 'and enjoying it. I've just made three good films. They've earned well, both for me and for the company, but if this one flops,' he shrugged faintly, 'the critics and the company will both kick me in the teeth without a qualm.'

Claire felt quite dazed, her cheeks flushed a delicate pink, her green eyes wide with amazement. She could hardly believe this was happening to her. She was actually standing here in the study having a friendly conversation with Jake Svenson. She felt she ought to keep pinching herself to see if she was really awake.

'I'm sure the film will be a success,' she said now. 'It's a super script.' Maybe it was presumptuous of her to try and reassure someone as successful as the director, but he didn't seem to mind.

'I hope you're right.' His brows quirked. 'But don't worry, you'll get paid anyway,' he teased with a smile.

'I'm not worried, I'm terrified,' Claire confessed with a shaky laugh. 'I've never been in a film before. I'm afraid I may make a complete mess of the whole thing.'

He shook his head. 'What can I say to convince you? You've no need to be worried, I promise you. Basically filming is no different from any other acting situation only it's the cameras that are your audience. You won't get any wild applause, of course,' he grinned engagingly, 'but they won't throw tomatoes either, although if you do get a polite request for an encore it won't be because I was pleased with your first attempt.' Even his voice had changed, Claire realised, the harsh drawling tones softened and warmed, inviting confidences.

'I always do get stage fright,' she told him now. 'Once I get the first scene successfully completed I shall feel much better.' One half of her brain kept telling her that she was a fool, talking to him like this and the other half kept on popping the words into her mouth.

The desk creaked as he leaned forward to emphasise his point. 'Try not to let it worry you too much, basically this is no different from your first stage appearance.'

Claire choked, the tiny moan of laughter startled out of her lips.

He watched her, stiffening, dark brows raised. 'Did I say the wrong thing?'

Claire shook her head. 'I'm sorry if that sounded rude, believe me it was hysterical laughter.' He was still looking puzzled and she sighed, wishing she'd never started this, knowing that she would have to explain. 'I'm afraid that my first stage performance was a complete disaster,' she confessed reluctantly. 'It wasn't my fault, not really. The production was appalling, and they'd cut corners every way they could to save money.' Claire had been staring at the polished floor but now she stole a quick glance at Jake Svenson. He was looking quite stern, she realised with a sinking heart, the blue eyes cool, the prominent bones of his cheeks settled into their old, harsh lines. And the problems hadn't been her fault, the director had been hopeless. She knew she would have to tell him the whole story, try and make him understand so that he smiled at her again.

He was still watching her in silence and she took a deep breath before saying: 'I was totally inexperienced of course. Maybe if I'd known more I could have avoided the pitfalls.' She stopped and sighed, pulling a small face. 'More likely I would have given the entire production a very wide berth. As it was I couldn't see any problems.' She fell silent for a moment, smiling to herself, remembering how naive she had been. The pay had been almost as poor as the production but it had been her first big chance. She had been sure she was already on the road to stardom.

'It was a very small part,' she continued quietly. 'I was on in the first scene. I had to walk on stage and close the door behind me, but unfortunately for me it was a draughty old building, somebody opened a door backstage, the wind whipped the handle out of my hand, the door banged, and very slowly, one entire half of the set started to fall towards me.'

'My God!' Jake Svenson sounded stunned. Claire glanced towards him and started to laugh. Maybe it wasn't very wise under the circumstances but she just couldn't help it, the laughter bubbled up inside her and wouldn't go away. It hadn't been funny at the time, of course, but in retrospect her remembered predicament seemed hilarious.

'What did you do?' the director asked now, his voice husky as though he was either trying not to laugh or was about to cry his eyes out.

Claire controlled her own giggles with an immense effort. 'More in the spirit of self-preservation than anything else I strolled very nonchalantly over to the wall and propped my hand against it. I pushed as hard as I could but it weighed a ton and my knees were buckling. Fortunately the male lead saw my difficulty and strolled over himself, ad libbing all the way.' Claire looked down at the floor and giggled again, remembering the horrified expression on the actor's face when he had realised what was happening.

'We spent the rest of that scene propping up one wall of the house and trying to speak our lines through gales of laughter from the audience and much quieter but far more ribald asides from the wings.'

Jake was laughing openly now, his eyes very blue, lingering with undisguised appreciation on Claire's expressive features.

'Lynn, my flatmate, said it was the funniest thing she'd seen in years,' Claire told him now.

His arms were folded across his broad chest. 'I'll bet,' he chuckled, and then: 'Who was the director, or daren't I ask?'

She told him, raising her brows in a question, but he shook his head. 'No, I don't believe I've ever met him, thank God.'

'I think he's teaching drama now.'

Jake pulled a face, half-smiling. 'Poor pupils! At least you won't have problems with the scenery here.'

Claire smiled her agreement but her reply went unheard. The door shot open and Marianne Lejeune sailed into the room, bracelets jangling as she walked towards the director. She embraced him warmly, her blue eyes sharp as they moved from one to the other of them, her lips smiling brightly.

'Darling, here you are,' she gushed. 'I've been looking everywhere for you. Isn't this cosy?' She paused and there was absolute silence in the room. Claire was very flushed. Marianne was making her feel guilty, which was ridiculous. The director had only been talking to her, that was all. He was staring down at his folded arms and Marianne smiled again, more brightly than before. 'Am I interrupting anything?' she asked looking at Jake. 'Tell me if I am and I shall leave you immediately.'

'No need,' he spoke at last, the smile on his mouth a trifle grim, 'Miss Grant and I had just finished.'

'Darling,' Marianne smiled, her voice gently chiding as she murmured, 'Miss Grant! How coldly formal. Really, Jake, how old fashioned of you. Everyone uses first names these days and Claire's a particularly attractive name. I for one intend to use it.' Her hands were still lightly looped around Jake's arm and she turned to smile at Claire, the warmth not quite reaching her eyes. 'That is, if you'll permit me to do so, my dear? And, of course you must return the compliment and call me Marianne.'

Claire smiled weakly. 'It's very kind of you. Of course you must call me Claire.' Marianne might be smiling but Claire wasn't fooled, the atmosphere had altered completely since she came into the room. There were undercurrents present which were impossible to read and which Claire told herself determinedly she didn't want to read. She hovered uncertainly now. The director was gazing at the floor, a moody expression on his hard features. Claire began to back away slowly. 'If you'll excuse me.'

Jake raised his head, his expression carefully blank. 'Fine, we'll see you later.'

Claire turned and fled, telling herself that she was happy to make her escape. Jake Svenson's attitude had changed so quickly she didn't know what to make of him. She was totally confused. Not that she would be given any opportunity to get to know him better, Marianne would see to that. Jake belonged to her. She had hung the sign on him very plainly this morning. The only question was, did he know it was there?

CHAPTER FIVE

THE next two weeks fell into a steady pattern for Claire. Mostly it was work and more work, rehearsals and filming occupying almost every daylight hour. By six-thirty every evening she was exhausted and once dinner was over and she'd read through her script for the next day, she wanted nothing more than to climb the stairs and tumble wearily into bed. Everyone on the cast complained of varying degrees of exhaustion. The only person apparently able to keep up the hectic pace without flagging being the director. He was tireless, directing, rehearsing and handling every problem that arose with the same unceasing energy.

Claire was watching him now as he discussed the next scene with the director of photography. The producer was there too, bent into a huddle with Jake and Al, his full mouth pursed in concentration. He was a big man, almost six foot four, and he towered over the other two, but still it was Jake who drew the eye. There was a whipcord strength, a steely magnetism about him that David Preston, for all his extra height and the power of his booming voice, simply didn't possess.

Claire was sitting on the cushioned window seat, partly hidden by the heavy maroon curtains and she altered position slightly now, drawing in her legs, anxious to see without being seen. Every time she saw Jake he drew her eyes like a magnet and even when he wasn't in her field of vision her thoughts seemed to find him without difficulty. He was being so kind and helpful she could hardly believe it. She had half-expected his attitude to change again after Marianne had come into the study and found them together, but it hadn't.

Only today he'd taken her to one side, discreetly,

while everyone else was having a coffee break. 'Don't play Désirée quite so furiously at this stage,' he murmured, looking down into her eyes, his expression setting her heart beating madly. 'She might spit and scratch, but not, I think, in this particular scene. She isn't sure as yet just what Trellisick's motives are, so play it cool, Claire.'

Claire had nodded, suppressing the desire for hysterical laughter. It was good advice, but slightly ironic coming from Jake's lips. She did need to play it cool. Jake was getting under her skin and she was letting him and like Désirée she didn't know the first thing about his motives. There were so many questions in her head and she didn't know any of the answers. Where did Marianne fit in, for one thing? She loved Jake, but did he love her? Claire sighed, uncoiling her legs as she saw that the crew were preparing to film the next scene. She hadn't a clue and she suspected that she wouldn't be any wiser when she left Ardwennan Manor in two-and-a-half months' time.

It was another week before Claire managed an evening away from the manor and when Mike invited her to have dinner with him at his hotel in the village she leaped at the chance. She realised that she was becoming obsessed by *Wrecker's Bride* and everyone in it and although in some ways this was a good thing— Désirée felt to be a part of her and not just a role she was playing—it frightened her too. She had rung her mother in the States and telephoned Lynn a couple of times but realised as she was talking to them that they could have been beings from another planet. She listened to their news and made suitable replies but it had meant very little to her, they had been part of a fantasy world to Claire, *Wrecker's Bride* and its cast had become her only reality.

She told herself that she had been working too hard and a night out in Mike's cheerful company was exactly what she needed. Even the thought of escaping for a few hours made her feel light-hearted and she hummed as she put the finishing touches to her make-up, slicking a layer of mascara on to her thick lashes and a soft pink gloss over her mouth. She'd already secured her hair away from her face with two diamanté combs and the delicate gold hoops in her ears swung gently as she pushed herself to her feet, drawing attention to the slender length of her neck revealed by the upswept hairstyle.

She walked over to the window, her hands spread on the stone sill, her face close to the glass. It was a clear night, stars piercing the navy blue sky, a pale sliver of moon throwing eerie shadows on the distant beaches.

She shivered suddenly. Although it was late April there was a feeling of frost in the air and the gauzy, blue material of her dress provided little protection. Claire glanced downwards; it was a very elegant frock and came with an equally elegant, floaty wrap, giving her tall figure a delicate almost ethereal air, but now she began to wish she had worn something else. Mike's car was hardly a Rolls and she would probably freeze to death before they even reached the hotel. She hesitated for a moment, but then with a faint dismissive shrug she picked up her evening bag and left the room.

Mike was already waiting in the courtyard when she went downstairs, the engine of the old MG quietly ticking over, and he gave a low, appreciative whistle as he helped her into the passenger seat and walked around to join her.

He smiled. 'Beautiful, Claire, the other guys will be climbing the walls with jealousy.'

Claire's cheeks were pink and although it was difficult in the confines of the small car, she struck an extravagant pose to cover her embarrassment. 'Just call me Cleopatra.'

'Cleopatra Grant.' Mike put his head on one side, pretending to consider it. 'Well, it certainly has an unusual ring to it.'

Claire laughed and settled back in her seat, prepared to enjoy the evening. It was lovely to be out with Mike.

She could relax, be herself completely without worrying what impression she was making. They laughed and chattered all the way to the village, Claire turning her head determinedly away from the terrifying drop as they climbed the narrow road from Ardwennan. It wasn't far to the village and the hotel was in the very centre, set back from the road, the engine of the MG straining a little as it climbed the steep drive.

They parked on the gravelled forecourt, Mike holding Claire's arm as she picked her way carefully over the pebbly surface towards the main entrance. It was a large, white-painted building, built more recently than the manor, but with a pleasant lived-in feel to it. It looked warm and welcoming and the heat and the noise and appetising smell of cooking hit them as they pushed open the door and walked inside.

The meal was delicious, tender local fish, and meat and fresh vegetables, all beautifully cooked. And Mike was in high spirits, Claire's soft laughter drawing all eyes to their table, her bronze-red hair and sparkling green eyes holding their attention long after the laughter had stopped. They took their coffee at the table and afterwards went to join some of the younger members of the cast in the cocktail bar. Claire was reluctant at first. They were a noisy, laughing group, crowding around the small table and she was afraid that they wouldn't want her, afraid that she would no longer belong.

She wanted to be accepted quite desperately. Everyone had been kind to her at the manor but she had missed the warmth and camaraderie of being one of a crowd. For a moment she felt quite sorry for herself. She had a foot in both camps and yet belonged to neither. She could feel depression settling in but Mike was walking forward and she forced herself to go with him, and then Peter Lister, a slim, dark-haired boy playing one of the villagers, had turned and seen them, waving in their direction, and the moment had passed.

'Mike, Claire, come and join us.' They were greeted

by friendly cries as everyone shuffled round to make more room for them at the table.

Claire sat quietly between Mike and Peter, sipping her drink, a smile in her eyes as she listened to the teasing banter going on around her. No wonder she'd been feeling depressed. This was what she'd missed, she realised. She was too much alone at the manor, she needed others who were in the same boat to help keep her feet on the ground.

'God, I nearly died! There was I practically starkers when Richard Angrams strolled into the room.' Claire had been lost in thought but the laughing voice claimed her attention, her eyes studying its owner with amusement. Lesley Heath always made her want to smile. The girl's features were all wrong, everything too big for her piquant face. But there was such lively warmth and intelligence in the brown eyes that you noticed nothing else once she began to speak.

Peter Lister was smiling too. He put his whisky glass on to the table and winked at Claire. 'Complain did he, Les?' he teased. 'What did he say? This is a disgusting sight. Remove this woman from the room immediately.' He did a fair imitation of Richard Angram's drawling, sexy voice and then ducked instinctively as Lesley threw an unopened packet of crisps across the table towards him.

'Oh you!' Lesley shook her head, her dark curls bouncing and then her faint pout dissolved slowly into a giggle. 'Actually he just stood there, taking it all in, me frantically clutching this miniscule towel around my middle. "Darling, how delightful," says he, you know, in that sexy way he has, his eyes all sort of big and devoted, hamming it up like mad. "Have dinner with me tonight." '

Claire laughed with everyone else but she could well believe Lesley's story. Richard Angrams had already acquired a reputation as the company Lothario. She'd had problems with him herself. He'd made a beeline for her when production first started, asking her out for dinner, sending her flowers, and he'd been angry when she turned him down. But she knew very well he was married, his wife telephoned the manor every day without fail. Claire suspected that she knew exactly what her handsome husband was up to and was trying to keep tabs on him the only way she could.

Lesley was still expanding on her conversation with Richard Angrams but Peter was not about to let her get away with it, he waited until she paused for breath and then grinned, 'So, what did you say to all this outrageous flattery? "Would you like me to wear my false teeth, or shall I leave them out? And what about this wooden leg, will it be in your way?" '

Lesley pulled a horrid face. 'Give me back that packet of crisps this minute, Peter Lister, so that I can throw them at you again.'

'Can't, I've eaten them.' He grinned, showing her the empty packet before crumpling it up and throwing it into the ashtray. He saw her face and laughed again, his blue eyes wicked with amusement. 'Okay, keep your hair on, Lesley.' He fished into his pocket and passed a pound note across the table. 'Go and buy yourself some more crisps and get everyone another packet while you're there.'

Lesley left on her errand and Claire relaxed, allowing the talk and the laughter to wash over her once more. She was well fed, in good company and very contented. She allowed her eyes to drift around the room. It reminded her of a score of other bars in which she'd sat throughout the country, red-shaded lamps, polished wooden floors and tables, a few uninspiring prints on the cream walls. But it was comfortable, a huge log fire burning in the grate, a nicely arranged vase of daffodils and blue iris on each of the window sills.

The door opened, the noise from the public bar drifting into the room and Claire's eyes moving idly towards it. She sat up immediately, feeling her face whiten, her mood of relaxation instantly shattered. Jake Svenson had just walked into the room, sheepskin jacket opened to reveal a beautifully tailored dark suit beneath. He looked sleek and polished and to Claire very dangerous indeed. He stood just inside the door for a moment, gazing around the room and Claire stared at him as though mesmerised, her green eyes shocked, bewildered, her chest feeling as though she had just been kicked, all the breath knocked out of it.

Why was he here? Tonight of all nights, when she had so desperately needed to escape from Ardwennan and everyone in it. She could feel the angry tears pricking her eyelids and she bent her head to hide them, hoping that he was only a product of her imagination and that when she raised her head again he would have gone away. But he hadn't! On the contrary he was already walking towards their table, Lesley at his side, her arms full of crisp packets, her cheeks very pink as she gazed up at him, chattering excitedly.

And Jake was smiling down at her, but Claire sensed that his attention was wandering, he seemed to have eyes in the top of his bent head and somehow she knew they were searching for her. She felt a bit like a small brown mouse being hunted by a falcon and she shrank lower into her seat, trying to escape that invisible gaze. They had both stopped in front of the table and Claire knew without looking up that Jake was staring at the top of her head. What did it mean? Why was he here? Was she simply being oversensitive, imagining that he had come looking for her? Maybe the explanation was quite different.

There were so many questions and only he could supply the answers. She raised her head, driven by her need to know and her breath caught in her throat, the air she sucked into her lungs suddenly raw and painful. Jake's blue eyes blazed into hers and she couldn't look away. An extra chair had been brought and he lowered his weight on to it now, still holding her mesmerised gaze with his own. Claire sat and trembled, burning up as his feverish eyes licked over her face, touching her bare shoulders, moving to the soft, tantalising swell of her breasts. His eyes were so hot they were scorching her flesh, electric sparks leaping between them, Claire's heart thudding like a hammer in her chest.

Even when she tore her gaze away at last she still couldn't escape. People were talking and laughing all around her but she noticed nothing. She was in a small private world of her own where thoughts of Jake Svenson obsessed her. It wasn't Ardwennan Manor or the set of *Wrecker's Bride* from which she'd needed to escape, she realised now, it was Jake Svenson! Unconsciously she'd realised that he was growing on her mind and tried to break free, but it was a hopeless task. She had never been free of him from the moment they'd met at the audition. He had haunted her then and he was still haunting her. What did he want from her? Wasn't Marianne Lejeune enough for him? The angry questions flared in Claire's brain and she sat, rigidly silent, her shaking fingers clutching her wine glass so tightly that she feared it would break under the pressure.

Mike had been talking across the table to Fleur Denton, but as though he recognised Claire's silence, he leaned back towards her, dark head bent, eyes warm. 'Okay?' he murmured very quietly. 'Are you enjoying the evening?'

Claire raised her eyes, careful to avoid Jake Svenson's glance. 'It's been wonderful.' And it had, at least until Jake Svenson's arrival and she wasn't about to voice that exception, it would be far too revealing a statement. 'It's the most enjoyable evening I've had for ages. I needed a break badly.'

Mike agreed. 'You and me both. I know just how you feel.' He glanced quickly around the table. 'We're all exhausted.' They were talking in low intimate tones, their heads close together. 'Svenson doesn't look bad on it though.' He laughed softly. 'He's got Les practically swooning at his feet. I doubt whether even Richard Angrams can cope with competition like that.'

Claire had been conscious of Jake's deep, husky tones

and Lesley's delighted laughter for some time but had been determined not to look at them. She didn't look now. Instead she turned to Mike, her jaw tight. 'It has been a wonderful evening. I've enjoyed every minute of it but in all honesty I feel completely shattered. I need some sleep. Would it be too much trouble to run me home?'

'We'll go right away.' Mike smiled, draining the last of the beer in his glass. 'You do look pale. It's Sunday tomorrow, try and rest, stay in bed.' He pushed himself to his feet looking down at her. 'Maybe I'll get over later in the day and we'll do some sightseeing.'

'That would be lovely, Mike.'

Claire had tucked her evening bag under the seat and she bent to retrieve it as Mike addressed the table in general, 'Claire's tired, I'm going to run her back.'

There was a murmured chorus of regrets as Claire got to her feet.

'Come and see us again.'

'Yes, come tomorrow,' Peter chimed in, his eyes lingering appreciatively on her gently curving figure. 'If Mike won't fetch you give me a tinkle and I'll play chauffeur with pleasure.'

Claire could feel her colour rising. Jake was watching her. She just wanted to escape as quickly as possible. 'That's kind of you,' she murmured.

'But unnecessary.' Mike sounded quite belligerent. 'I'm more than happy to do any chauffering that Claire needs.'

Claire sighed, it was ridiculous, Peter and Mike were quarrelling over her like jealous lovers and it was totally untrue. She daren't look at Jake Svenson. She didn't need to be a mind reader to know what he would be thinking. 'Shall we go?' she murmured, tugging at Mike's sleeve.

'No need for you to turn out again this evening, Brent.' The director's tones were brusque to the point of rudeness and Claire's eyes swivelled towards him of their own volition. His whisky glass was empty and he was already on his feet, fastening the heavy buttons of his sheepskin, and he was watching her, his blue eyes intent on her face. 'I'm going back myself. I can give Claire a lift.'

Claire turned her head, sending Mike a frantic look of appeal. Maybe she was being foolish but she didn't want to be alone with Jake. There was something in his attitude this evening which frightened her, made her feel vulnerable and defenceless.

Mike took the hint immediately. His eyes on the director he said, 'It's kind of you to offer, but I don't mind taking Claire. It's early yet, there's no need for you to break up the party.'

'Yes, do stay, Jake.' Lesley was smiling up at him, a pleading hand on his sleeve. 'Have another drink with us.' She looked across the table. 'Pete's buying.'

He laughed but shook his head regretfully. 'I'm afraid I must go. I'll have that drink with you another time,' he promised. 'But some of us have to work tomorrow.'

There were groans of mock sympathy all round.

He grinned, his hands deep in the pockets of his overcoat. 'Yes, a director's life is hell, isn't it? I'm glad to see you're all so sympathetic.' Before the laughter had completely died down he turned back to Claire, his dark brows raised, his face a carefully controlled mask. 'Ready? Shall we go?'

'Please, I . . .' Claire shook her head, not knowing what to say. What objections could she make without seeming completely crazy? He was offering her a lift that was all, not asking her to run away with him.

Mike was still trying to help. 'I don't mind turning out,' he persisted quietly.

Jake sighed, his face cold, all lingering traces of laughter vanished. 'I do realise that, but where's the point? I have to go back to Ardwennan anyway and there's plenty of room in my car for two.' The words were clipped, daring Mike to disagree with him.

'Thank you, it's kind of you to offer.' Claire spoke

quickly, not wanting to cause trouble for Mike, and she could see that Jake was beginning to get angry. She said her goodbyes, sending Mike an especially grateful smile and followed the director out of the room, trying to think reassuring thoughts all the way.

They were half-way across the public bar before he spoke to her. 'You're shivering.' His voice was low and intimate and came from so close to Claire's ear that she jumped visibly. 'Don't you have a coat?'

She wasn't shivering she was trembling but she wasn't about to tell him that. 'No, I didn't bring one,' she murmured huskily.

'You're crazy, do you know that? It's freezing out there.' His voice was still low but there was a thread of anger running through it, his eyes on her face willing her to turn and look at him, so that she forced herself to stare rigidly ahead, apparently totally absorbed in picking her way through the crowded bar. The room was packed, people everywhere, clutching glasses, laughing and chattering and although Jake attempted to cling to her elbow they kept getting separated by the crowd. It didn't improve his temper any.

'Did you hear what I said?' he growled now in her ear.

'Yes I heard.' Claire kept on walking. 'But I'm okay. It's only a short drive back to the manor and I'm not cold.'

'Like hell!' he snapped. She could hear him breathing at her side in short angry jerks. 'Brent must be as crazy as you, letting you come out half-naked on a night like this.' She could feel his eyes wandering over her bare shoulders again. Cold, who was cold? Not she, she was on fire, tiny flickers of feverish heat swimming along her veins. She hated him because he could make her feel like this. But she hated herself even more. She would have liked to have felt nothing when he looked at her, instead of which she felt weak and shaky and had to keep reminding herself that this was Jake Svenson.

'I never get colds. I won't hold up production, don't

worry.' She meant to say all that in a cool little voice but it came out in trembly jerks. What was he trying to do to her? Did it amuse him, playing around with her emotions like this?

They had reached the door of the hotel now and when he opened it she stalked through, her head high, trying to put as much distance as possible between them. She strode along as quickly as she could on her high heels, so deep in her own thoughts that when a warm coat suddenly descended on her shoulders, it took her completely by surprise. She stopped in her tracks, snuggling involuntarily into the soft wool. Jake was right behind her, gripping her shoulders.

'Is that better?' he murmured, his warm breath fanning her cheek. He had leaned forward to speak so that his hard body touched her own, the heat from it piercing the thick jacket, searing her flesh beneath.

'Yes, thank you,' she whispered. She could scarcely frame the words and they came out as a husky whisper.

His grip on her shoulders tightened, pulling her back, moulding her pliant body to his own. 'Are you angry because I offered to bring you home?' he breathed against the soft skin of her neck. 'Maybe it wasn't wise, but I wanted to see you alone. I've been trying to talk to you for days now, but there's been no opportunity.'

Claire knew he was talking and she absorbed his words without conscious thought, her heart beating so fiercely she thought it would burst. His hands had slid from her shoulders, inside the open jacket, closing around her waist, his mouth on her neck and ear and cheek blazing a trail of tiny, tormenting kisses. She was all feeling, all emotion. The night sky pierced her with its beauty, the stars twinkling only for her, the distant sound of the sea a faint echo of her own loud heart beats.

They both heard the sound of the hotel door opening, the voices and laughter carrying easily to where they were standing locked together in silent embrace, and Jake's reaction was immediate. He released her, so that she swayed dizzily for a moment, welcoming his hand beneath her elbow as he urged her towards the car park. They walked along in silence, Claire not daring to look at him, wondering if she had imagined the last few minutes when he had held her in his arms.

He slid her into the front seat of the car, still without a word, walking around to join her, his powerful body completely relaxed, looking as sleek and expensive as the low-slung sports model he was driving. Claire watched him through shadowy lashes. What am I doing here? she thought with wild incredulity. I must be crazy! But still she sat there, watching his lean hands as he switched the engine into purring life. She couldn't stop looking at him and this time he was watching her, the expression deep in his eyes telling her that she ought to jump out of the car and run for her life while the running was good.

'Ready?' The simple word and the look he gave her were full of caressing warmth, sending tiny shivers up and down Claire's spine.

She nodded her agreement helplessly. No one had ever made her feel like this before. She was a crazy jumble of confused desires and emotions. Jake Svenson at the heart of every one of them.

The car moved off at last, the powerful headlights cleaving a path through the inky darkness, the wheels crunching noisily over the gravel surface and then swooping down the steep slope and on to the deserted road. Jake was quiet at first, all his attention given to the road ahead and Claire couldn't have broken that silence to save her life, gazing instead out of the window, seeing nothing, her shaking fingers clasped tightly in her lap. Her reaction when he held her in his arms must have been painfully obvious, she realised. He must know she had wanted him to kiss her, make love to her. She wished that she had more pride, that she could control the way her heart leaped whenever he came near to her. But she wanted him and there seemed no way she could alter that feeling.

She risked a brief, sideways glance at his hard profile and then looked away again quickly. He seemed to shimmer at the edge of her vision. Powerful, silent, like a predator waiting to pounce, and she was undoubtedly his prey this evening, Claire realised with a tiny inward shiver. She was staring at his face quite openly now, without even being aware of it and he turned suddenly, catching her eye.

'Comfortable?' He smiled into her eyes.

'Very, thank you,' she murmured, her cool little voice belied by the hot flush staining her cheeks.

'Warm enough?'

'Yes, thank you.' Claire wanted to lower her heavy lids and block his face from her vision. His eyes were dark and deep and she was drowning in their blue depths.

'We're nearly home.'

'Yes.' She made herself turn and look out of the window. The powerful headlights pierced the darkness, showing her that they were already on the road to the manor, but even their precipitous situation had no power to disturb her at the moment, her entire being was absorbed by Jake, there was no room for anything else. Claire watched his capable hands on the wheel, liking their strength and their long, slim, powerful shape, remembering the feel of them on her body when he had held her, wanting them to touch her again.

They had stopped outside the manor before he spoke to her again. He turned in his seat, his lean body very near to hers, his words taking her completely by surprise. 'What is Mike Brent to you?' he murmured, his blue eyes very intent on her shadowed face. 'I've been watching you over the last few days, he clings to you like a leech, and he didn't want me to bring you home this evening. Why was that? Is he in love with you?' His voice was very quiet but he rapped out the questions as though he was determined to get an answer. Whatever Claire had expected him to say it hadn't been this. It felt almost as though he had struck

her in the face. She burned with indignation. Mike had
only been trying to help her; she refused to let Jake's
nasty, suspicious mind spoil their relationship.

She could feel herself bristling, her chin up, her green
eyes spitting fire. 'Mike Brent is married,' she gritted
through tight lips. 'As I'm sure you know very well. His
wife is one of my oldest friends, I would never
knowingly do anything to hurt her.' Jake was watching
her with a white, set face but she barely noticed. She
took a deep, trembling breath. 'I know exactly what
you think of me, Mr Svenson, and maybe my behaviour
in the past has given you cause, but I'm not in the habit
of having love affairs with married men and I don't
intend to start now.' She drew herself up to her full
height. 'If you're going to take this clean-up campaign
to its logical conclusion, might I suggest that you begin
with some of the better known members of this
company and stop picking on me.'

She was so angry she could have cried, she knew she
had to get out, into the fresh air, before she broke down
completely. She released her seat belt and groped with
shaking fingers for the door handle, but just as her
hand closed over it Jake's arm shot out, clamping like
an iron band around her midriff, so that she struggled
frantically, gasping for breath.

'Let me go!' she cried as he ignored her struggles.
'You've brought me home as you intended. You've had
your chance to insult me, now take your hands off me!'

She could see his face through her half-closed lids. It
was hard, his cheek bones taut and shiny, a faint blue
shadow darkening his chin, gleaming eyes staring down
into hers. Claire felt her heart miss a beat and began to
struggle even more wildly.

'Keep still!' His voice was low and hoarse, his hard
fingers pinning her arms to the seat. 'I'm not going to
let you out just yet, not until I've had a chance to talk
to you.'

Claire kicked out with her feet trying to catch his
ankle but she missed, her actions simply causing him to

tighten his hold. 'Insult me don't you mean?' she grated through clenched teeth. It didn't matter what she did, it seemed he would always think the worst of her.

'That was never my intention.' He was breathing hard, the rapid pounding of his heartbeats beneath the dark suit, pacing Claire's own. 'I've told you, Claire, I want to talk to you.'

'Well I don't want to talk to you!' Claire exclaimed. He was so close she could see every pore, every tiny indentation on his tanned skin. She could feel her mood changing, the anger dying. If she didn't escape now she knew she never would. She began to wriggle frantically and he moved closer, one hand sliding beneath her hair, his hard fingers gripping her neck.

She gasped aloud, 'You're hurting me!'

His expression was grim. 'Stop struggling and then I won't.'

'I want to get out!' She pushed helplessly at his chest, feeling the heat of his flesh beneath her hands, knowing that he had won whatever she said.

Somehow he sensed her silent capitulation. He relaxed, a warm gleam in his eye as he stared down at her. 'Just let me say what I have to say before you go,' he demanded huskily. He watched her for a moment and then smiled. 'That's better.' He touched her cheek with gentle fingers. 'I'm sorry, Claire. Truly, I didn't mean to upset you.'

He was far too close. His face only inches from hers, and she turned her head, staring determinedly out of the window, 'Just say what you have to say and let me go.'

'Don't be angry.' His voice was low, pleading, playing on Claire's vulnerable emotions. 'I did know Brent was married,' he murmured softly. 'Sure I did, but he could have been waiting for a divorce, separated for years from his wife for all I knew.' His fingers had slipped back to her neck, but it was different now, there was no pain, only pleasure as they stroked her soft skin with an insidious, tormenting rhythm. 'Don't go cold on me Claire,' he whispered. 'I know we haven't always seen eye to eye in the past but I thought all that was behind us.' His voice was soothing, the tones seductive, wooing her, breaking down her resistance, so that she could feel her taut muscles relaxing, her head turning with a small uncontrolled jerk so that their eyes met.

It was dark in the car but she could see them gleaming only inches away from her own and she could hear the way his heart was pounding, echoing her own wild pulse beats. He was going to kiss her! The knowledge was like a drug invading her veins and making her blood sing, and her lips parted softly, a silent instinctive invitation as she forgot everything except the fierce need to touch him and feel his arms around her.

The beam of light which suddenly erupted across the front of the car broke the spell as effectively as a bucket of cold water would have done. Claire pulled out of Jake's arms as though their touch had scalded her. She was shaking, every nerve ending in her body crying out for the kiss which had just been denied her. It was as bright as day in the car and she could see that Jake looked almost as shaken as she did herself.

'Claire!' He was leaning towards her as though he intended to take her in his arms again, but she jerked backwards out of his grasp. She had seen who was standing in the lighted doorway even if Jake hadn't. It was Marianne and Claire couldn't face a scene, not tonight. Let Jake handle it. He was the one with the complicated love life.

He put out a hand, but again she evaded him, scrabbling desperately behind her for the door handle and when she found it, almost tumbling out of the car in her eagerness to escape, Jake's coat still clutched tightly around her shoulders. She climbed the steps to the brightly lit porch on trembling legs, feeling the silent anger pulsing from Marianne's figure as she passed her. Claire knew she had made a deadly enemy tonight, but it was an emotion worlds away from fear which kept her awake far into the night, listening to the distant sound of the surf on the rocks, but hearing only the confused and tormented workings of her own brain as she tried to make some sense out of Jake Svenson's confusing behaviour.

CHAPTER SIX

THE next morning she felt dreadful, huge shadows darkening her eyes, her skin pallid, every nerve ending in her body screaming to cower back under the duvet and simply not have to function any more. But she dragged herself out of bed anyway, standing for a long time under the shower, allowing the cool spray to wash away some of the accumulated tension, her mind a deliberate blank. She had been worrying half the night and it had got her precisely nowhere. Her thoughts were a mess and she refused to let them torment her any longer.

She skipped breakfast; even the thought of food made her feel sick. Instead she made a cup of coffee with the equipment she had in her room and sipped it slowly, on her feet, staring out of the window. The sky was blue, feathers of white cloud scudding across its broad canvas and she could see the path from the house climbing away over the cliff top. Suddenly she felt a great longing to be out in the open. The walls of the old house seemed to be closing in on her. She needed fresh air and exercise.

Once she'd decided it took only a few minutes to get ready. She was already dressed in an old pair of jeans and a T-shirt and with a heavy knitted jacket thrown over her shoulders to keep out the sea breezes she was soon out of sight of the manor, striding along the close-cropped turf, the breeze lifting her hair, blowing soft bronze-red strands around her face. There was a faint spring-time smell of green and growing things in her nostrils and the broad vista of sun and sea and sky soon brought the sparkle back into her green eyes again.

She walked briskly along, allowing her thoughts to wander anywhere but back to the manor and its occupants. She thought of her parents in the States and decided that she would pay them a visit as soon as the film had ended. She would be able to afford it now, of course, and maybe Lynn would be able to go with her. Last time Claire had spoken to her she'd been very optimistic about her own career. Claire smiled as she thought of her friend. Lynn had worked hard; it was good that her career had taken off at last.

Claire walked for miles that morning, her knitted jacket over one arm, her face turned greedily towards the first hot sunshine of the year. There were a few other ramblers on the path, couples walking dogs, family groups with children trailing along behind their parents. Claire greeted them all cheerfully, her naturally high spirits surfacing again for the first time in weeks.

It was the pangs of hunger which finally drove her back to Ardwennan, fresh air and exercise increasing her natural appetite. But the homeward path seemed to wind in front of her like a never-ending ribbon and her stride was flagging long before she topped the rise leading to the house. Even so she stood a moment and gazed downwards. The old house still dreamed in golden sunshine, its windows reflecting a million prisms of light, smooth green lawns surrounding it, their borders nodding with spring flowers.

It was a welcome sight and Claire began to run, taking the grassy slope at full speed, entering the building by the front door, her pace barely slackening as she climbed the stairs. She turned the corner at the top, still at full tilt and it was only Mike's alertness which saved them both from a painful collision. Claire jumped as strong hands shot out and gripped her shoulders, her startled cry turning to a sigh of relief as his brown eyes smiled reassuringly down into hers.

'Mike, thank goodness! I wondered who it could be. For a moment there I was terrified.'

Mike had dropped his hands and was laughing at her now. 'That's nothing to the way I feel, believe me, being suddenly confronted by a red-headed battering ram charging at full tilt around the corner.'

'I'm sorry.' Claire's green eyes were dancing, all trace of her earlier depression banished by the fresh air and the sight of Mike's cheerful face. 'I didn't expect anyone else to be around. Its such a gorgeous day I thought everyone would have fled the building.'

'So they have if they've any sense,' Mike agreed. 'Which incidentally is why I'm here. I thought you might like to go into Penzance for afternoon tea, scones and clotted cream. How does that sound?'

Claire groaned, her face twisted into a grimace of pure anguish. 'Don't Mike, you're torturing me! I haven't had lunch yet and I'm starving.'

'That's settled then. We'll go into Penzance. I'll buy you lunch.' He grinned, flicking her pink cheeks with a teasing finger. 'And you can treat me to scones and clotted cream. And maybe we can look around the town afterwards, act like ordinary tourists for a change.'

'Lovely,' Claire sighed. She had deliberately evaded the thought of how she would spend the rest of the day, once lunch was over, but it had niggled at the back of her mind all morning. She didn't know whether Jake and Marianne were spending the day at Ardwennan but she did know that she had no wish to meet them, not today. Once she saw them she knew she would have to start thinking again and her brain simply felt too exhausted to cope.

Mike was still watching her, hands in the back pockets of his jeans, one shoulder propped against the wall. 'Coming then, Claire?' he asked.

Claire nodded, raking one hand through her dishevelled hair. 'Yes, if you don't mind waiting until I've changed.'

His eyes flickered over her curving figure appreciatively. 'I don't know what you're expecting, but we're going to a back street caf' not the Ritz,' he teased.

Claire laughed. 'I still have to fetch my bag and run a comb through my hair.'

'Okay,' Mike agreed cheerfully. 'I think I can manage to wait that long.'

Claire was heading towards her room almost before he had stopped speaking and Mike ambled along behind her, sticking his head around the bedroom door as Claire sat at her dressing table already drawing a brush through her dishevelled hair, soft curls spilling over her face.

'So this is how the other half live?' He sauntered into the room looking around him. 'Not bad.'

Claire laughed, bending forward to peer into the mirror as she flicked a light coating of mascara over her thick lashes. 'Be honest, it's no more comfortable than your room at the hotel, is it?'

Mike grinned at her reflection in the mirror and then walked to the bed, stretching his length on the cotton duvet, arms behind his head, blue trainers dangling over the edge in an attitude of complete relaxation.

'Less comfortable, actually,' he agreed with a self-satisfied smile. 'This bed's not bad though,' he added, closing his eyes.

Claire turned, her tone dry as she said: 'I see you've made yourself at home anyway.'

'Hmm,' he murmured, 'this is very nice.' Claire smiled, he looked completely at ease and the sudden hammering on the door didn't seem to disturb him any. 'Answer that will you, Claire. I'm busy at the moment.'

Claire threw the brush she was holding so that it landed on his leg with a thump and he jackknifed into a sitting position.

'Ouch, that hurt,' he wailed bitterly, rubbing his thigh where the missile had landed. 'I'll get you for that. See if I don't.' And then he grinned fiendishly, threatening her with his clenched fist.

Claire was already half way to the door. She pulled a face. 'You and who else?' she mocked. She jerked it open, still laughing and then foa second her power of speech dried up completely. Jake Svenson was standing on the threshold, a navy T-shirt emphasising the muscular width of his shoulders, white jeans moulding the powerful length of his legs, but it was his eyes that

drew her startled gaze and held it. They seemed to have
lost all colour, as cold and unfeeling as the arctic sea,
moving from her flushed face, the laughter dying on it,
to Mike's still figure, half-sitting, half-lying on the bed.

'I'm sorry to disturb you, Miss Grant. I can see
you're busy at the moment.' His blue eyes dripped ice
down her spine, the clipped, formal words loaded with
contempt. 'I came to collect my coat, but maybe you
could leave it with the housekeeper later today and I'll
fetch it from her.'

Claire stared at him with haunted green eyes. She
wanted to shrivel up and die. All the thoughts and
emotions she'd been suppressing during the morning
rushing back to torment her. She was attracted to Jake
and she wanted to be with him, it was as simple as that.
Except that now it was too late! One look at his face
told her that. He thought she and Mike were lovers! He
thought she'd lied to him yesterday when she had
denied the fact!

He was still watching her, his lip curling cruelly as he
saw the tears filling her eyes and the way her soft mouth
trembled. And he leaned forward, his voice soft and
grating so that only Claire could hear, 'You're a
brilliant actress, Miss Grant. You almost have me
believing you.' He smiled unpleasantly. 'I must
apologise for coming to visit you at such a difficult
time, although if I'd realised you needed a man quite so
badly I would have collected my coat a couple of hours
earlier!'

Understanding came slowly to Claire and then she
gasped, the colour gradually draining from her cheeks,
leaving her pale and trembling with pain and anger at his
insulting words. Her hand shot out, making contact with
his taut cheek almost before she was aware of it. She
would have taken it back if she could, but it was too late.
She watched in horrified silence as his hand flew to cover
his face where she had slapped him, his body rigid,
smouldering fury in the glance he turned on her, so that
she shrank back instinctively from its silent threat.

'I'm sorry . . . I'm sorry,' she whispered painfully. 'I didn't mean to do that. It's true, please, Jake . . .'

He breathed in a huge rasping breath, his molten blue eyes locked on to her pleading face. 'Never, never do that again!' He shook his head slowly, threateningly. 'And be thankful that this film is already well on its way or, believe me, today would be your very last day in employment.' He straightened abruptly, dropping his hand from his cheek where she had branded him, her splayed finger marks clearly imprinted in red on his flesh. He leaned towards her again and she forced herself to stand her ground. 'One last word of warning,' he gritted from between clenched teeth. 'Stay away from me, stay well away or God knows I won't be answerable for the consequences.'

With one last fierce glance full of loathing he turned on his heel and was gone. Claire closed the door, leaning back against it, her head sunk on to her chest as she tried to control the threatening tears. Mike had been shocked into silence during that brief, angry interchange but now she could hear him coming towards her. She raised her head, forcing a smile to her lips. She wouldn't allow Mike to see the pain that Jake had inflicted. She wouldn't allow anyone to see it. She was infatuated with the man but like all infatuations it would pass. The pain was a temporary thing. By this time next month she would have forgotten that she'd ever experienced it.

Mike was the soul of tact. Seeing that she didn't want to talk about her unexpected visitor he swallowed his curiosity, watching her with anxious eyes but going out of his way to distract her, so that it wasn't until she'd climbed in bed and switched out the light later that evening that she had time to reflect on Jake's visit. Consequently she tossed and turned half the night, like someone in the grip of a feverish illness, and Monday morning was agony. Even the shower failed to refresh her. She stumbled down to breakfast still in a half-dazed state. Fortunately at six-thirty in the morning everyone else seemed to feel the same. Good mornings were muttered from behind newspapers and conversation was minimal. Neither Jake nor Marianne were in the room, which was a considerable relief to Claire. She drank a cup of tea and ate a slice of toast and began to feel a little better.

She left the dining room as quietly as she'd entered, intending to go straight to the small room the make-up girls were using for their work, but drawn instead to one of the partly opened mullions. It was a beautiful morning with a blue, rain-washed sky, and the silver birch just outside the window was already unfurling its bright green leaves, a blackbird singing sweetly somewhere in its branches. Claire listened entranced and when she turned around Dave Tillson was already standing beside her, his beaming smile as warm as ever.

She smiled back at him but stiffened a moment later when he told her that he had a message from Jake. 'Don't tell me I've got the sack already.' She tried to joke about it but she could hear the wobble in her voice, her words weren't really so funny. Remembering the way Jake had looked at her yesterday she knew that firing her had been one of the least violent of his urges.

'No,' Dave's brown eyes twinkled, 'it hasn't come to that yet. In fact I'm the bearer of good tidings.' He beamed. 'You can go back and spend the rest of the morning in bed. We've changed the shooting schedule today. You won't be needed until five o'clock.'

Claire stared at him in horrified silence, her face twisted into a grimace of false delight as he went on to tell her that as it was such a perfect spring morning they were to use it to advantage and film some of the outdoor scenes, including her own cliff-top love scene with Bryce David. Claire had always hated Mondays but this was ridiculous! She left Dave and climbed the stairs to her room sunk in depressing thought. Of all the scenes in *Wrecker's Bride* this was the one she'd been dreading most. Set on one of the highest cliffs in the area, the drop was awesome and she still hadn't told anyone but Mike about her fear of heights.

She ought to have told Jake, she realised that now, when it was too late. But she'd kept putting it off, not wanting anything to spoil their fragile new relationship. The smile she gave as she opened the door to her room was ironic. That relationship had been damaged irrevocably in a way she couldn't have foreseen and she was the very last person to whom Jake would give a sympathetic hearing today. She would have to master her fear of heights very quickly. He had hurt her yesterday. She refused to give him yet another opportunity to turn the knife in her wounds.

The arc lights illuminated Claire's terrified countenance as she raised pleading eyes to Bryce David's face. Under the circumstances it wasn't hard to simulate a pleading expression. Terror was too mild a word to describe Claire's emotions. Her worst fears had been realised. She had spent all afternoon giving herself good advice, but it hadn't worked. She was still petrified. She could almost feel the cliff edge, yawning emptily only inches away from her bare feet and she couldn't resist another backward glance, her hand clutching frantically at the rough cloth of Bryce's ragged sleeve.

'Christ! What is this? A film set or a bloody Sunday school pantomime?' Jake's snarling tones erupted on to the set once again and Claire watched with wide, apprehensive eyes as he stalked pantherlike into the circle of light. She had never seen him quite so angry before. His body, tilted slightly forward, was stretched taut like a bow string. Any minute he was going to snap and Claire was under no illusion as to where the arrow would fall.

He stared at her, his eyes flashing dangerous blue flames. 'What the bloody hell's the matter with you today? That's the tenth time we've had to shoot the same scene!'

Clearly he expected an answer, but Claire was mute,

her tongue frozen to the roof of her mouth. She stared helplessly, the wild scene graven indelibly into her brain: the blazing red sunset catching them all in its fiery glow, the frozen faces of the camera men almost out of range of the arc lights; the cameras themselves, monstrous and silent as they waited for their cue to begin rolling again.

But Bryce clearly felt none of her reluctance to break the silence. 'Claire keeps clutching at me,' he complained. 'She's done it every take so far.'

Claire didn't altogether blame Bryce for his words. He'd been under the lash of Jake's tongue all evening too. He must be as exhausted as she was herself and, what's more, he knew she was to blame for the constant re-takes.

'I can see that all too clearly.' Jake's head had jerked around, those cold blue eyes on Claire again, stripping the last ounce of her self-confidence. 'Do you have any reasonable excuse to offer, Miss Grant? Do you have a headache perhaps?' He was moving closer, his dark shape looming powerfully in the weird light of the arc lamps. 'Maybe you've had too many late nights recently?' he continued remorselessly. 'That would seem a likely explanation. What time did you get in this morning? Two . . . three o'clock?' He paused, his pitiless gaze raking Claire from top to toe. 'Perhaps you should pay more attention to the job in hand and less to your other dubious pleasures.'

Claire couldn't look at him. She couldn't let him see just how much he was able to hurt her. She focused her eyes somewhere over his left shoulder, seeing the amazed faces of the crew ranged behind him. They were as shocked as she was herself by the way he was behaving. He was still watching her, his eyes cruel, waiting for her to speak. Somehow she forced her dry lips to move, her words coming out as a hoarse whisper. 'I'm sorry! It's true, it was my fault. But I am trying my best, honestly.' Her green eyes were wide, pleading with him for understanding, but he was merciless, leaning

over, close to her shaking figure, his flickering shadow
enveloping Claire in its darkness.

'Your best doesn't seem to be good enough in this
instance, does it?' he grated. 'I must admit I find it
rather difficult to understand. This is a love scene and I
thought they were your forte!'

Claire thought that she would have preferred an
angry snarl to the smile he gave her then. 'Don't please,
don't!' The trembling in her limbs was growing worse.
His hatred was stripping her emotions raw. She
couldn't take any more. She could feel the hot tears
pricking her eyelids and she knew he must have seen
them too, but her vulnerability seemed to increase his
anger rather than lessen it.

He raised his eyes heavenward. 'Tears now, would
you believe! For Christ's sake, woman! You're
supposed to be a professional actress, not a two-year
old!'

His face was a mask of cold fury and Claire knew she
was going to break down completely. Why was he
doing this? It was tearing her apart. It was almost as
though he wanted to destroy her. The tears which had
been threatening began to spill down her cheeks and she
raised trembling fingers to wipe them away. While he
stood and watched her, lean hands clenched into fists at
his side, as though afraid if he relaxed them, they would
reach out and shake her of their own volition.

'I'm sorry,' Claire choked.

'You're sorry! My God, we're all sorry, believe me!'
He was a wild figure as he raked one hand through his
dark hair. For the moment he seemed to have run out
of words and no one else spoke, stunned into silence by
his unprecedented behaviour, but as Claire watched he
took a deep, steadying breath.

'Now hear this.' He faced Claire, his expression as
pale and strained as Claire's own. 'I shall give you one
last opportunity to get this right, and if you don't . . .'
He stopped, shaking his head, his expression grim. 'Just
get it right! Just get it right, that's all!'

The tears were pouring unchecked down Claire's face now and she just stared at him, wishing the ground would open and swallow her up. He turned away abruptly as though he couldn't bear to look at her any longer.

'Get the make-up girls out here immediately, Dave,' he shouted over his shoulder. 'And for the Lord's sake tell someone to bring a handkerchief. Miss Grant's about to put another couple of gallons into the ocean.'

He stalked away, his figure in the dark leather jacket swallowed up into the darkness beyond the arc lights almost immediately. Claire could feel her legs giving way beneath her and would have sunk weakly on to the grass if it hadn't been for Bryce David's supporting hand beneath her elbow. He had never been one of her favourite people but now she leaned against him as though he was her only salvation and when he quietly handed her a clean handkerchief she sent him a grateful glance with eyes still swimming in tears.

His own expression was slightly shamefaced. 'Are you okay?' he asked. 'I'm sorry I landed you in it. I didn't expect to provoke that reaction from the director.'

'You didn't, don't worry, Bryce,' Claire sniffed, dabbing rather ineffectually at her face with the handkerchief. She knew that whatever Bryce had said, Jake would still have vented his fury on her.

Bryce watched her efforts with the handkerchief for another moment and then removed it from her hand with a half-impatient gesture, turning her face to the light as he wiped the moisture from her cheeks. He was a handsome man, with the sort of dark, good looks which sent the fans wild, but he was a loner and Claire had written him down as unfriendly, but now she began to revise her opinion.

'The whole mess this evening has been my fault,' she told him and he listened intently as she explained about her fear of heights.

'You little idiot,' he said when she had finished. 'Why didn't you tell Svenson? He would have understood.'

Claire doubted it. She shook her head. 'I don't think he would have understood anything this evening.'

But she understood, or thought she did. Jake was furious because he'd found Mike in her bedroom yesterday and this was his way of making her suffer.

Bryce was looking over his shoulder to where Jake and Dave Tillson were standing in conference and Claire followed his eyes reluctantly. 'I don't know what the hell's got into Jake today,' he muttered. 'It's going to be a barrel of laughs if he stays in this mood.'

The arrival of the make-up girls put an end to further speculation and Claire was soon outwardly calm once again, although inwardly she was as shaken as ever. Jake was destroying her and doing it in public. She ought to hate him. She wanted to hate him, but in fact she could only hate herself. His fury today had changed nothing for her. She was still attracted to him. However badly he behaved, she knew with horrifying certainty that one smile from him and she would be as weak-kneed as she had ever been, willing to forgive and forget.

All too quickly they were ready to resume filming and Claire approached the scene with a sinking heart. Another tongue-lashing like Jake had just given her and she would turn tail and head for home, and damn the consequences.

Bryce was still concerned about her. 'Try and forget about that cliff edge,' he murmured in her ear now. 'I've moved as far away as I dare, and I'll hang on to you, Claire, don't worry.'

Claire smiled gratefully up at him. 'Thanks, Bryce, I'll do my best.'

Jake was just at the edge of Claire's vision, the arc lights throwing his hard profile into sharp relief and he spoke now, 'When you've quite finished this cosy conversation perhaps we can begin.' The brief rest clearly hadn't improved his temper and his eagle eye had detected Bryce's new position. 'You've moved, Bryce. Angle a few inches to your left,' he instructed with an impatient hand.

Bryce shifted uncomfortably on the spot. 'Aren't we okay here?' he asked, shooting an appealing glance towards the cameras where he knew Al Denton, the director of photography, was standing.

Jake was in no mood to take opposition from anyone this evening. 'No, you bloody well aren't okay there!' he yelled. 'And when you've a question to ask, ask me and not the camera man. I'm the director of this film. Although the Lord knows at this moment I'd happily relinquish the position to the first idiot willing to take it!'

Bryce still hadn't moved and Claire tugged gently at his arm. He'd tried and she was grateful but Jake was looking more and more angry with every minute that passed. Bryce stayed exactly where he was, a stubborn set to his lips. 'I don't really think a couple of inches makes that much difference,' he persisted.

Claire sighed shakily but no one heard her, everyone was too gripped by the spectacle of Jake Svenson, hands on jean-clad hips, expression furious, facing Bryce David's white-faced but determined figure.

'If I say it makes a difference, be sure it does,' Jake grated harshly.

Bryce stood his ground bravely. 'Actually I'm terrified of heights,' he admitted, staring the director straight in the eye. 'It would help if we could stay here.'

Jake groaned aloud, a harsh explosive sound and Claire took a half step forward and stopped as Jake's eyes saw the movement and fastened on her. 'It isn't Bryce, it's me!' She thought she had never been so scared in her life before, her voice sounding ridiculously low and wobbly. But it was no good, she couldn't allow Bryce to take her punishment. 'I'm the one who's scared of heights.' Claire's explanation trailed away as Jake continued to stare at her, his eyes glittering orbs in the pale mask of his face.

'You mean we've been filming this scene over and over again and if you'd told me we could have solved the problem in the first minute?' He was incensed. 'You

stupid, idiotic little . . .' Claire thought he was going to
reach out and shake her and she shrank back
instinctively into the circle of Bryce David's arm.

Jake stopped short, his breathing ragged and uneven
as he stared at her in tormented fury. 'Move a foot
away from the edge.' He paused, his expression grim.
'And get it right this time or I shall feel like altering the
script and throwing you both over together!'

Claire's performance improved dramatically once
they were away from the yawning drop, but Bryce must
have been more disturbed by his brief argument with
the director than he cared to admit. Even Claire could
tell that his performance was stiff and awkward and
Jake stopped them just as Bryce's murderous fingers
around Claire's throat had turned to a rough embrace.

He strode on to the set, raking a hand through his
dark hair. 'Cut!' he bellowed. 'That's it! I've seen
enough!' He sighed heavily, looking at Bryce. 'You're
supposed to be crazy about the woman in your arms.
For God's sake, man, you're going to defy your entire
village and spare her life. Look as though you mean
that kiss.' The glance he threw in Claire's direction was
brief but she was naked under it, his eyes searing her
flesh. 'Whatever complaints I might have about Miss
Grant, I would have thought she was eminently
kissable.'

Claire stared at him in stunned reaction. What did it
mean? What was he trying to do to her? There had been
passion and desire in his eyes just then. How could he
look at her like that one minute and the next, have such
hatred in his eyes? It didn't make any kind of sense and
she could only think that he was trying deliberately to
upset her. And it had worked only too well, damn him!
Upset was a mild word to describe her feelings. He was
still instructing Bryce but she didn't listen. She kept her
head down and stared hard at the ground, not looking
up until Bryce strode forward ready to begin filming the
scene once again.

This time it was better. Claire put all the warmth she

could muster into that shared kiss, determined not to give Jake any further cause for complaint.

'Okay!' Jake strode into the light. 'That was better, much better.' He turned to Bryce. 'But it still lacks passion. The guy has problems. Feel it in your guts.'

Dear God, Claire thought, he isn't the only one. She was exhausted both emotionally and physically and it was pure desperation that gave her the courage to speak. 'Do you mean you want us to do the whole thing again?'

Jake's fiercely narrowed eyes were locked on to Claire's face. 'That's exactly what I do mean, Miss Grant. You've got it in one.' The black eyebrows arched in sardonic question. 'Do you have any objections? Through your stupidity we have already endured twelve takes.' His voice was silky smooth, the mockery there for everyone to hear. 'Surely one more, at my request, is not asking too much?'

Claire didn't know where she found the strength, but she made herself meet his eyes. The take had been good. It seemed that for some perverted rason of his own he was still intent on punishing her. 'I thought it went well,' she insisted quietly.

His jaw was clenched tight. 'And you're qualified to judge, I suppose?'

'I just thought . . .' She shook her head, closing her lips on the words. What was the use? He hated her! He wouldn't listen to anything that she said. And his next words merely confirmed her fears.

'Don't bother to think, Miss Grant!' he said tightly. 'You're not paid to think! When I want someone to do so I'll employ them for the quality of their brain. But let me remind you that you were simply employed as an actress. I don't require anything further from you than that you learn the script and do exactly as I tell you. Is that understood?'

With every harsh syllable his anger grew and Claire bit her lip, her silent nod of agreement a jerky unco-ordinated movement. She no longer had the will to defend herself. In fact she had no defences against his unreasoning anger.

But just then she felt Bryce stir beside her. 'I thought we did okay too,' he said with a faint shrug, his eyes wary, watching Jake's reaction to his words. 'Hell, Jake,' he added quietly, 'I don't think I'm going to be able to better that performance.'

Jake raised his clenched fists to his forehead as though driven beyond endurance. 'Give me strength!' he groaned. 'You thought you did okay!' He moved forward in two angry strides. 'Well you didn't! It was rubbish! It seems I've got to show you what I want.'

He elbowed Bryce to one side as though he was a lightweight, turning to Claire, his fingers gripping her shoulders with cruel emphasis. Claire couldn't believe it. She was in a daze, knowing exactly what was going to happen but powerless to prevent it. She stared at Jake helplessly, her green eyes huge and vulnerable in her pale face.

Jake was looking at Bryce rather than at her. 'Watch closely!' he commanded. 'Make yourself feel the violence and confusion of the man's emotions. You want her! You hate her!' He looked down, his eyes glittering strangely, pinning Claire with that glance. His fingers were hard and they slipped from her bare shoulders to close around her throat, burning her soft flesh. But she barely noticed. She was held by that fierce gaze and the mixture of wild emotions on his face. When his hands released her neck and jerked her body roughly against his hard length she realised it was exactly what she had been wanting him to do since they had first met. She closed her eyes, dizzy with the smell and feel of him as she swayed in his embrace and he gathered her closer, his lips fastening hungrily over her own so that she clung to him helplessly, her arms sliding involuntarily around his neck, her fingers tangling in the thick darkness of his hair.

She'd forgotten her surroundings. She'd forgotten everything except that this was where she wanted to be

and that he wanted it too. She could feel every inch of
his hard body and she knew that whatever else, he did
desire her. Even he wasn't a sufficiently good actor to
simulate that particular emotion and she responded
shamelessly to his touch, uncaring in that moment who
was watching. She was lost on a burning tide of feeling,
her mouth opening willingly to his searching tongue,
her body pressed wantonly against his own.

Her return to earth came with frightening suddenness.
One moment she was in the hard circle of his arms and
the next he had released her, leaving her blinking in the
cold light of reality, her limbs trembling violently in the
aftermath of that passionate kiss.

'That's how I want the scene played!' Jake muttered,
abruptly.

Claire barely registered the director's hoarse, un-
natural tones or the way his gaze lingered almost
compulsively on her bewildered features. She could see
Bryce walking towards her and she put out a trembling
hand, needing his support, leaning against him like a
child.

'Are you okay?' he breathed in her ear. 'You look a
little shaky.'

Dear God! Shaky was hardly the word to describe
how she felt. She scarcely knew what had hit her. She
had been kissed before, but never like that. But she
nodded, 'I'm all right, just a little tired.'

Jake was watching them with their heads together, his
face tight, blue eyes blazing. 'If you've quite finished,
I'd appreciate some action!' he snarled.

He was still furious. That moment in his arms had
altered nothing, Claire realised. She followed Bryce
obediently into the glare of the lights, keeping her head
down, refusing to look in Jake's direction. Her response
to his kiss had terrified her. She had had no defences.
But it had meant nothing more to him than a passing
moment's desire. She wanted to cry, but she carried on,
blinking back the tears, following Bryce's lead.

In fact he nursed her through that scene and she was

still in a daze when Jake finally called a halt to the shooting. She walked back to the house, Bryce at her side, her brain still in a whirl. What was she going to do? she wondered. How could she face the director after this? And would she ever understand him? She had begun to doubt it, and she knew that speculation was a pointless exercise. Jake wasn't for her! He never would be! And she had better accept the fact and put him out of her mind with all possible speed, instead of crying for the moon.

CHAPTER SEVEN

EVEN the vista across the walled garden and over the green lawns towards the sea had begun to pall and Claire put up her hand to shade her eyes, her head turning yet again towards the impressive frontage of Ardwennan Manor. There were still half-a-dozen figures grouped around the sound equipment. Al Denton had just placed the damaged boom back in position but there was still no sign that the crew were ready to begin filming.

Claire sighed. The last few weeks had been hell. She hadn't been sleeping and it showed on her face and in the weary attitude of her body as she slumped on the wooden seat. Her life was a mess. She would be the first to admit it, and this morning's delay wasn't helping her state of mind. She had three difficult scenes to play later today, two of them with Marianne, and that in itself was a far from reassuring thought. Oh, in public Marianne was pleasant enough, but Claire wasn't fooled. Marianne's jealous eyes shot red-hot sparks whenever Claire encountered them.

If she hadn't been feeling quite so miserable, Claire would have laughed at the irony of the situation. Marianne had no need to feel jealous of her, Jake made his dislike very plain. On the few occasions he couldn't avoid looking at her his eyes were so cold you could skate on them. He'd never lost his temper with her again, not after that evening on the cliff top, but Claire sometimes wished he would do so. His icy indifference hurt more than his anger had done. She was still reluctant to probe her own feelings too deeply, they were too painful for that, but certainly indifference was one word she would never use to describe them.

There was a brief flurry of activity from the front of

112

the house and Claire's attention was momentarily distracted by it. Jake had just walked out of the house. Claire was too far away to see his face clearly, but still her eyes were drawn towards him. She knew it was foolish but there was nothing she could do. He was like a drug, slowly poisoning her system. Although she knew he was dangerous she couldn't seem to leave him alone.

It was ten-thirty before the equipment was finally repaired and Claire feared that the delay would probably have upset her concentration. But to her joy, her stumbling, bare-footed run towards the manor went into the can immediately. Jake had been watching the take, but now he turned away, ignoring her, as she sat on the bottom step of the porch, the drab, ragged skirt of her peasant costume spread around her, trying not to hope too hard for a word of praise or even a simple acknowledgment of her presence.

He continued to ignore her. Claire bit her lip. It was only what she had come to expect over the last few weeks but it still upset her. Dave came up, his words warm and congratulatory, but it wasn't enough and when he turned away to issue directions to the crew her eyes slid back towards Jake, fastening on the dark-browed face bent intently over the script.

He looked tired, she thought, lines of tension pulling at his mouth, and clearly he hadn't had time to shave this morning, the blue shadow darkening his chin adding another dimension to his rakish attraction. She was so intent on her own thoughts that he'd raised his head and met her gaze almost before she was aware of it. She drew in her breath on a small startled gasp, feeling the wild pounding of her heart beneath her ribs, wanting to gasp for air. His eyes were eating her alive, that hot, fierce gaze lingering on her mouth, reminding her irresistibly of that moment on the cliff top when he'd held her in his arms and kissed her.

'Excuse me, Claire!' She jumped to her feet automatically as the lighting camera man strode in front of her, a coil of wire clutched in his brawny arms, and that momentary contact was broken. When she looked again Jake had swivelled around and his back was now towards her, broad-shouldered and uncompromising, the script flattened against a metal strut supporting one of the cameras, his attention apparently completely absorbed by it. While Claire stood and shook with reaction.

How could he turn his back on her after the way he had just looked? She wouldn't believe it had meant nothing to him. For the sake of her sanity she couldn't believe it. She understood very little about what went on in Jake's head, but that brief, unguarded expression must have meant something. He felt more than indifference towards her and she clung to that knowledge like a lifeline, no longer even trying to pretend to herself that she didn't care.

There was a pile of equipment to be moved before the crew would be ready to shoot the next scene and Claire wandered back in to the hallway, her bare feet welcoming the touch of the cool, stone floor, her mind still torturing the same familiar topic. Slowly she wandered over to examine the pictures on the white-painted walls. They were serene landscapes, pictures of the Cornish countryside painted at every season of the year. They were soothing, and almost without realising Claire became absorbed, so that when Marianne came to stand beside her, resplendent in the blue silk gown required for her role as Lady of the Manor, Claire felt none of the trepidation she might otherwise have done. Even so she didn't like the way Marianne was smiling at her and it took an effort to turn and face her, returning that smile with one equally as false.

'Claire, my dear, I'm so pleased to find you alone,' Marianne gushed. 'There was a little matter I wanted to discuss with you.' Marianne looked even more exquisitely beautiful than usual, Claire thought, her glorious hair arranged in an elaborate coiffure, her make-up equally as skilful. But all the mascara and eye-shadow in the world couldn't hide the glittering malice in her eyes and if Claire hadn't been worried before, she was now, her calm smile pinned to her face with glue. It helped that they weren't alone. The hurrying feet and raised voices of the production team had irritated her earlier but now she could only be thankful for their presence. Maybe she was being over-imaginative but Marianne's smiling malice seemed to pose an actual physical threat. Claire could almost feel those long nails raking her face and it was hard not to show her fear.

She kept on smiling politely. 'Is something wrong?' she asked now. 'Has there been a change in the schedule?' She knew it couldn't be anything so simple but ignorance seemed to be her best defence, and one look at Marianne's face had told her that she would need one.

'Not that I'm aware,' Marianne answered smoothly. 'It was something else that I wanted to discuss. A matter which concerns us both.' She raised her delicate brows. 'Do I need to go on, my dear?' She paused with exaggerated emphasis. 'No, I'm sure I don't. You're a sensible girl. You know exactly what I'm trying to say.'

Claire shook her head, her eyes guarded and watchful. 'I'm sorry, I don't understand.' But she did, only too well. Jake was the subject Marianne wanted to discuss with her and he was the very last person Claire wanted to talk about.

Marianne wasn't fooled by Claire's denial. 'Oh come along, Claire,' she said. 'Don't let's play games. We're too old for that. Believe me, when I say that I've seen it all before. I've known Jake for a number of years and you aren't the first to fall for his undoubted charm. Indeed, I have every sympathy with you, I quite see why you're behaving like this. But really, my dear, it won't do. It's creating an immense amount of embarrassment and the gossip is making things difficult for Jake.' She regarded the perfect oval of her nails in silent concentration for a moment. 'I promised him that I would mention the matter to you. We both felt sure you'd understand.'

Claire was very pale as she absorbed the full meaning of Marianne's words. But despite the anger and contempt with which he sometimes treated her it was somehow inconceivable that Jake had discussed her with Marianne. She couldn't and wouldn't believe it. This had to be Marianne's idea. But did it? What did she know about Jake after all? Practically nothing! Claire's face was a blank mask as thoughts fought for precedence in her brain. She was torn, not knowing what to believe, but whatever doubts she suffered she had no intention of showing them to Marianne.

'I really don't know why you're telling me all this,' she said, her chin up, her green eyes vivid in her pale face.

'My dear girl, I think you know very well.' The malice in Marianne's eyes was turning to anger, but Claire had no intention of letting it intimidate her.

'On the contrary. I haven't the slightest idea what you're talking about. If you're suggesting that I'm attracted to the director then all I can say is that you're widely off the mark.' She shrugged in a masterly parody of unconcern. 'If you've heard that he kissed me—passionately—during the course of filming, it is true. But I'm sure you don't need to worry,' she added in a kindly tone. 'I didn't allow it to go to my head, I promise you.' Claire was acting her head off, her words as forced and unreal as a badly scripted play, but still they got to Marianne. Her cheeks paled until they were chalk white beneath her make-up. Claire couldn't repress a surge of primitive satisfaction. Maybe it was foolish to antagonise her, but at least her words had brought Marianne's anger and enmity out into the open. It was easier to avoid a blow when you could see which direction it was coming from.

Marianne was glaring at Claire now, her blue eyes deadly. 'Don't think this air of unconcern has me fooled for a moment,' she hissed. 'I don't know what you hope to gain, but you're behaving very foolishly. Believe me, I can make things very difficult for you.'

'You can try of course. But really, unless you have some ulterior motive, I can't see why you should want to do so,' Claire countered, her own eyes sparkling angrily. She half turned. 'If you'll excuse me, I think I need some fresh air before we film the next scene. The atmosphere's getting a little unpleasant in here.'

Before Marianne could think of a suitable reply, Claire had whisked around and marched out through the open door, but not before she'd recognised the expression in the other woman's eyes. If Marianne could hurt her, she would. Claire was under no illusions. But the damage was done and she wasn't sorry. Marianne's words had deserved that response and given the same provocation Claire would have repeated her replies exactly, word for word.

When Claire left Marianne, she wandered outside still fuming, but it was a lovely morning and as she walked along the gravel paths in front of the house, her temper slowly subsided. A rose-pink daphne was in bloom just outside the door and she bent to smell it, the perfume lingering long after she had left it.

Ardwennan Manor was beautiful, she reflected dreamily. In other circumstances she would have adored living there, but of late she had begun to feel homesick for London. She longed to see Lynn's friendly face again, even the noise of the traffic and the constant hectic pace of the city seemed admirable in retrospect. And she needed to get away from Ardwennan if only to put her worries into perspective. They had grown out of all proportion in the last few weeks, like outsize tropical plants in a hothouse, fed by overheated emotions simmering beneath the surface. It would all seem so much easier if she could escape in the evenings, go back to the flat and laugh over the day's events with Lynn. Her sense of humour had deserted her completely in recent weeks. She had gone broody, like a mother hen. She only hoped she wasn't going to lay a giant-sized egg by challenging Marianne as she had done today.

She was still wandering around in the garden when

Dave came to tell her that they were ready to shoot the next scene. She was justifiably nervous, having to face Marianne again so soon, and this time in front of the cameras, but in fact she was proud of her own performance. It was Marianne herself who interrupted the scene when she collapsed weakly on to one of the high-backed chairs which had been in the St Avon family for generations, Claire studied her bare toes intently, not needing to raise her head to know that Jake was walking across the room towards them. She was embarrassed, she realised. Marianne's accusations seeming to hang in the air between them. She was half afraid that he would stop and say something too, but he walked on past her, addressing himself to Marianne.

'What went wrong?' he asked quietly and even the most insensitive ears must have recognised the weariness in his tones. He sounded exhausted. Claire didn't want to feel sympathy for him, her feelings were already too confused without adding to them, but she simply couldn't help her reaction. She risked a quick glance. The lines of strain on his face were deeper than ever. She longed to reach out and smooth them away with gentle fingers.

'Darling, I'm exhausted!' Marianne's plaintive tones drew Claire's attention and as she watched Marianne pressed trembling fingers to her pale temples. 'The delay this morning,' she continued. 'And now, having to film this particular scene.'

Jake raised dark brows, the eyes beneath them shadowed and weary. 'I'm sorry about the delay,' he sighed. 'I would have avoided it had I been able.' He paused, broad shoulders moving in a faint shrug. 'But as to the filming of this scene, I'm not aware of any particular problems.'

'Darling, I don't want to cause you any more difficulties, you know that.' Marianne rose to her feet and stepped towards him, her fingers smoothing the frown from his brow as Claire had longed to do. Claire dropped her eyes, feeling the twisting knife of jealousy in her stomach. Damn Marianne! She knew Claire was a reluctant audience and she was deliberately flaunting her privileged position, taunting Claire.

Claire dropped her eyes, studying the worn flagstones at her feet. She refused to play the game Marianne's way. She refused to watch and she didn't listen either, not until she heard her own name on Marianne's lips, and then her head jerked up, her green eyes incredulous. She just couldn't believe what she was hearing.

'It's difficult working with Claire.' Marianne's words were tentative, with just the right amount of regret in her tones. 'I don't like to say this. I know she's relatively inexperienced and we have to make allowances.'

Claire was staring, open-mouthed. She had to say something in her own defence even if no one believed her. But her mouth stayed open, Jake's deep, husky tones taking her completely by surprise.

'I never make allowances for any of my cast, no matter how inexperienced. You should know that, Marianne.' His eyes flicked in Claire's direction, a faint glint of amusement in their depths as he saw her expression of idiotic amazement. Claire closed her mouth quickly, listening to what else he had to say.

'Let's give it one more try.' He smiled gently at Marianne. 'And leave me to worry about Claire's performance. Be assured that I will step in if I see the need.'

Claire was still gasping for air. Jake had actually defended her. She still couldn't quite believe it. And she wasn't the only one shocked by Jake's reply, Marianne was furious. But Jake didn't seem to notice. He strolled back across the room towards the cameras, his hands thrust deep into his trouser pockets.

'Let's take it from the top,' he told them and it was Claire instead of Jake who experienced the full blast of Marianne's anger.

'Don't think you've escaped so easily,' she muttered

the moment Jake was out of hearing. 'You haven't seen anything yet!'

Claire refused to listen. She was still floating three feet above the ground. Amazingly the director had been unsympathetic to Marianne's complaints. What else could she do, after all? Claire was not left to wonder for very long. There was one hiccup after another in the smooth running of the next scene; one-and-a-half hours later they seemed to be further away from success than ever. When Jake called, 'Cut!' yet again, Claire could willingly have crawled under the highly polished antique table and hidden her head in her hands. She knew she had omitted half Désirée's most important speech. Marianne had sabotaged the early takes one subtle way after another and by the fourth take, as she'd intended, Claire's nerves were so shot to pieces that she began to make her own mistakes without any prompting.

Her eyes flew across the room now to where Marianne was talking to Jake, her head confidingly close to his. The light from the window falling across them, separating them from the shadowy room, increasing their intimacy. Claire realised that Marianne was probably pouring out complaints about her performance into Jake's ears and she couldn't expect him to defend her this time. Marianne had accomplished her sabotage so skilfully that Claire herself hadn't realised what was happening. Not until it was too late. Marianne had certainly won this round, Claire reflected bitterly. She only hoped it wasn't the final victory.

'Jake wants to speak to you in his office.' Claire's head jerked up, startled by Dave Tillson's quiet approach.

'Oh no,' she sighed and then pulled a small face. 'Okay, Dave, thanks for telling me. I'll see you later. Always assuming I survive this interview in one piece.'

'Don't worry,' Dave murmured. He was smiling gently, his brown eyes conveying his sympathy. 'Jake's not blind. He could see what Marianne was doing.'

Claire couldn't allow herself to hope and her voice was gloomy, resigned almost as she said: 'Then why didn't he stop it? He must have known how I felt.'

'You've got to remember that Marianne's the star. To put it bluntly, my love, the film can't do without her. He's got to be tactful. You'll just have to let him handle it his way.'

Dave's words were meant to be reassuring but had quite the opposite effect on Claire. 'And it can do without me, I suppose,' Claire returned, unable to hide her bitterness.

'Don't be an idiot! Haven't I just said that Jake realised what was happening? Go into the office and stop worrying so much,' he urged her, taking her elbow and giving her a tiny push in the direction of the door. 'You're playing right into Marianne's hands at the moment. Go and listen to what Jake has to say before you jump to any more conclusions.'

Claire could feel Dave's sympathetic eyes on her back as she left the room. At least he had noticed what was happening and that in itself was vaguely reassuring, but still she faced the closed door of Jake's office with a feeling akin to blind terror, her stomach twisted into knots as she raised a trembling hand to knock on the wooden panels. His hard tones responded immediately to her shaky tattoo and she pushed open the door and stepped into the room, her chin high, only her green eyes mirroring the tension she was feeling.

She stopped just inside the door, her gaze flying instinctively to the desk where she expected Jake to be sitting, but in fact it was Marianne, lounging very much at her ease in the brown leather swivel chair, who encountered Claire's first glance. The raised chin and erect stance didn't fool her for a moment, she knew that Claire was afraid and she smiled maliciously, directly into Claire's eyes, her face hidden from Jake by the curving wing of the chair.

Claire took a deep breath, her hands balled into fists at her side. Marianne wasn't going to get the better of her without a fight, she decided angrily. She turned her head deliberately, her eyes searching the room. Jake was disposed elegantly against the fireplace, his body a graceful arc, his dark lashes sweeping his cheeks as he gazed with apparent absorption into the empty grate. And even at this inauspicious moment Claire felt the pull of his dark attraction. She didn't want to flush or hear her heart pounding so loudly against her breastbone, but she couldn't control her bodily reaction. She knew she was a fool, totally idiotic, but then cold logic had never had a place in her feelings for him.

She pulled herself together with a jerk, realising that Jake was watching her now, his blue eyes hooded and enigmatic. 'Would you like to sit down?' he asked, indicating the chair to one side of the desk.

Claire shook her head. 'No, thank you,' she murmured. She would feel less at a disadvantage on her feet. Less aware of the bedraggled state of her peasant dress and her bare, dirty feet.

Jake accepted her refusal without comment. He studied the toe of his boot narrowly for a moment and then raised his head. 'Before I make my own observations do either of you have an explanation to offer for this morning's poor performance?'

Claire pressed her lips tightly together. She did have an explanation, but how could she voice it? And if she did, who would believe her?

'Darling, surely it's obvious.' Marianne's drawling tones broke the silence. 'This is Claire's first film role. I don't want to be unkind, but I really do think that she's simply out of her depth.'

Claire lifted her head, her eyes stormy with frustration. Anything she said in her own defence would sound like a pathetic excuse after that little speech of Marianne's, but if only for the sake of her pride she couldn't let the accusation pass without at least trying to defend herself.

She kept her eyes fixed on Marianne. 'It was you!'

she cried, the words throbbing with anger. 'You deliberately caused the problems in the early takes! You knew it would unsettle me!'

Jake was still silent, his watchful eyes moving from one to the other of them like an umpire at a tennis match.

Marianne's beautiful face was a picture of distressed bewilderment. 'My dear girl, why ever would I do such a thing? I was already exhausted before we started filming. I was as anxious as Jake to complete the scene.'

Claire fumed silently. Marianne's reply sounded so reasonable, how could she ever hope that Jake would understand? 'It was all an act and you know it,' she told Marianne angrily now. 'You were furious with me and that was your way of making me suffer. I know you're going to deny everything and I know Jake won't believe me.' She shook her head, 'I find it difficult to believe myself. You're a star! Surely you ought to be above this sort of petty behaviour!' Claire's words were wild and unconsidered, but she was too angry to care.

Marianne cared! She sat up abruptly, her eyes on Jake, her air of relaxation punctured by Claire's accusing words 'Are you going to let her speak to me like this?' she snapped. 'She's made a complete hash of this morning's performance. She's quite clearly totally unsuited to the role she's been given and now she's seeking to blame her own inadequacies on me.' Marianne was hurling the words at Jake, her blue eyes furious, all pretence of friendship for Claire forgotten. Now she turned to Claire, 'As for you, Claire Grant, I've been making allowances all morning for your inexperience, but no longer. I haven't the slightest intention of continuing to work with you, not today, not any day!'

'None of that is true! You know it's not!' Claire's bronze-red hair swung wildly as she shook her head in agitation.

'If you've quite finished.' Jake's icy tones cooled Claire's overheated emotions as effectively as a cold shower. He straightened, facing them both, his expression grim. 'Now hear this,' he stated coldly. 'I'm the director of this production . . . for my sins. You've told me a number of times that I'm too easy with my cast, Marianne. Well, maybe you're right. Maybe I have been, but not any more. Believe me, this is where the kid-glove treatment stops.'

He was a forbidding figure; tall and lean and dark, his strong-boned features thrown into sharp relief, blue eyes glazed with ice. Claire trembled inwardly, guessing what was coming and dreading to hear it. If he banished her from the film, not only would it mean a ruined career but she would probably never see him again. It was an unbearable prospect and she watched him with anxious green eyes as he began to speak again.

'I refuse to have my two principal actresses quarrelling like a pair of spoiled schoolgirls. God damn it! You're supposed to be professionals! Let's see you both behaving as though you are!'

Claire's jaw dropped open yet again. He was actually sharing the blame between them. She couldn't believe it.

Marianne couldn't believe it either, her face a picture of stunned amazement. 'Jake darling,' she vibrated angrily, 'you can't be serious. You heard what Claire said to me. Surely you're not defending her?'

Jake sighed, his fingers wearily massaging his neck beneath the open collar of his shirt. 'I'm not defending anyone, Marianne. I'm simply trying to make a film. The morning's been a fiasco from beginning to end and I'd just like us all to begin work again at the earliest possible moment.'

Marianne was outraged. 'You mean that you're still intending to keep Claire Grant on the cast?'

He was watching Claire's face, his eyes shadowed by his half-closed lids, but now he nodded curtly, 'She stays.'

Marianne had pushed herself angrily to her feet. 'You can't be serious.' She moved towards Jake, her arm sliding through his, her face upturned in tremulous appeal. 'Darling Jake, don't do this to me, please. Don't you care that she's insulted me? Don't you care that she's ruined the morning's filming?'

Jake covered Marianne's fingers with his own, his expression softening as he gazed down into her face. 'Try not to upset yourself like this,' he murmured gently.

'How can I help it?' Marianne sniffed emotively, her fingers tightening on Jake's arm. 'I've been shouted at and insulted . . . and I was dead on my feet before we started filming.'

Claire felt like a member of the audience at the first night of a play. Marianne was laying on the pathos for all she was worth, her soft lips trembling, her blue eyes shimmering with unshed tears, and Jake seemed to be lapping it up, his voice low and intimate as he tried to reassure her. Claire refused to watch. She would have liked to have crept out and left them to it, but instead her eyes wandered around the room, examining the books and the pictures on the walls, trying to block their low-voiced conversation from her brain but never quite succeeding.

Marianne seemed to have successfully convinced Jake that she was completely exhausted by the events of the morning and it was with no great sense of surprise that Claire raised her head and saw them both walking towards the door, Jake's arm supporting Marianne's weight.

'Marianne's going to lie down in her bedroom for an hour,' he told Claire as he was passing. 'But please sit down and wait here for me, I want to do some work on the script with you before we start to film again.'

Claire flopped into one of the comfortable leather armchairs when the door had closed behind them, her head back, her eyes closed. She didn't expect Jake to hurry back. Now that Marianne had him in her clutches she was sure he wouldn't escape so easily. And she didn't even know whether he would want to escape. She still had no clear picture of his relationship with

Marianne Lejeune. Were they lovers or weren't they? Claire sighed heavily now, her expression moody. What did it matter? Whether he was free or not, Jake wasn't interested in her. She had begun to think that her main problem was an overactive imagination. One brief exchange of glances and she was reading things into it which clearly weren't intended.

She got to her feet, walking over to the bookshelves which covered one wall of the small room. It was hopeless trying to relax. Her brain wouldn't let her. It was far too active and there only seemed to be room in it for one subject.

She was reading through an old copy of *Twelfth Night* when Jake entered the room, her head bent, totally lost in Shakespeare's beautiful prose, and it was the growing feeling of eyes on her back which made her turn slowly to face the door. He was watching her, an expression on his face which brought the blood rushing to Claire's cheeks. But then he moved, closing the door with a bang and the moment had gone so completely that Claire wondered once again if her imagination was playing tricks on her.

'I'm sorry to have kept you,' he stated abruptly, walking across the room and dropping into the swivel chair which Marianne had recently vacated. He didn't look sorry, Claire thought. He looked angry, his face cold and hard. It made Claire nervous and she almost dropped the book she was holding as she turned and thrust it hurriedly into the vacant place on the shelves.

'I'm sorry,' she murmured apologetically. 'Did you mind me looking at the books? I thought you'd be some time . . .'

He was still watching her, his blue eyes narrowed, his shrug noncommittal. 'They're St Avon's property not mine. But I'm sure he would have no objection.'

Claire swallowed nervously. This was terrible. She wished he wouldn't keep staring at her like that. 'I've still got the two books you lent me a few weeks ago,' she ventured tentatively. 'I must remember to return them.'

'And have you read them?' He looked bored by the entire conversation, lying back in the chair, his eyes half-closed. Claire couldn't understand why he'd asked her to wait here for him. He appeared not to have the slightest interest in her. She was so busy with her thoughts that his questions had barely registered on her brain and he raised his dark brows, his eyes very blue beneath them.

'I assume from the silence that you haven't read the books.' He sounded bored and irritable and Claire flushed. 'There's no need to feel embarrassed,' he said. 'They weren't required reading. I don't normally issue book lists to my cast.'

'I did read them,' Claire countered instantly. 'Well, I finished one of them and I have started the other.' Her flush deepened under that blue, faintly disbelieving stare. It was true, she had enjoyed the books. But unfortunately the moment she opened the yellowing pages, disturbing memories of the morning Jake had shown her around the house would come rushing back into her mind. So she had pushed the leather-bound volumes into her bedside cupboard and firmly shut the door on them. But she couldn't explain that to Jake. He would think she was crazy. Instead she said, 'I just don't seem to have had enough free time to finish them.'

Jake was gazing at the ceiling, his hands clasped over his lean stomach in an attitude of complete relaxation and Claire wondered crossly whether he had listened to a word she'd said. 'Perhaps I ought to go now,' she stated tartly. 'I do know the script well enough. And I can see that you're frantically busy.'

She turned, making for the door, but he rose to his feet at the same time and was there before her, blocking her way. 'I'm sorry, that was rude of me.' And then he laughed, his eyes warm, gleaming down at her. 'Apologising to you is becoming a habit.'

Claire refused to be charmed. 'You don't need to apologise,' she told him. 'I do know I've been a nuisance this morning. I do realise that you're busy.'

He was still smiling appealingly at her. 'I was rude. It was inexcusable. But I was preoccupied. Quite frankly there's so much to do that I just don't know where to start. And something else has just come up. I'm afraid our discussion about the script will have to be deferred.'

Claire didn't believe him. It was just an excuse because he didn't want to talk to her. 'That's quite all right,' she said through tight lips. 'I understand.' She tried to step around him to reach the door, but he moved again so that she couldn't pass.

'You don't believe me.'

'Of course I believe you. I know how busy you are.' Was that her voice? Claire wondered, shocked. It sounded ridiculous, the tones high and forced, the words brittle. But he was standing far too close for comfort, the smooth brown sweep of his muscular throat only inches away from her eyes and she daren't look up, frightened of what he might read on her face.

He was still intent on giving her an explanation. 'I had a phone call a few minutes ago. I have to go into Penzance to clear some documents with the bank.'

Claire stared at him, her eyes wide, wondering why he should even care that she believed him.

He shook his head, raking a hand through his dark hair. 'For God's sake, Claire!' He sounded exasperated. 'I know you've had one hell of a morning. This is not a deliberate evasion on my part. I'm not trying to make the situation worse than it already is.'

'Why should I believe you? You've treated me like a leper for weeks. I realise that you'd probably like to carry on avoiding me.' Claire knew she sounded sulky, but that was exactly how she felt. He'd been horrible to her for weeks. This sudden change of heart was a little hard to take.

'I know, I've been bloody angry with you!' Jake sighed now. He was leaning back, propping his shoulders against the door in an attitude of weary resignation. 'I've behaved like a bastard, Claire. I'm aware of that, but God knows, you've given me plenty of provocation.'

Claire felt her eyes widening in amazement and amusement flickered briefly on his face. 'Don't look so surprised, Claire. I'm willing to admit that I jumped to conclusions with very little evidence.'

'I'm sorry, Jake. I know it did look suspicious when you came to my room. But Mike's just a friend.' Claire's voice was low and husky and involuntarily she made a move towards him. But clearly it was the wrong thing to do. Even though he didn't actually retreat she sensed his instinctive withdrawal.

'We'll take it as read, that we're both suitably apologetic then,' he said with a faint smile and then he bent his head, glancing ostentatiously at his watch. 'I must ask you to excuse me now, Claire. I have to leave in thirty minutes and I still have to shave and change.'

Now that he was so eager to get rid of her Claire was stubbornly reluctant to go. It seemed she was forgiven but not completely. He was still holding himself aloof. And she didn't want that. She wanted them to be friends again, she wanted him to trust her. And if he was to do that they needed time to talk.

Jake had opened the door and he was standing beside it now, a polite smile on his face but Claire hesitated, carefully avoiding his eyes, 'I was wondering.' He waited in silence and Claire took a breath and plunged ahead, 'If we're to have a free afternoon, would it be possible for you to give me a lift into Penzance? I have some shopping to do, and not having a car of my own it's difficult . . .' Her voice trailed away. She could feel him watching her, his eyes piercing the top of her head.

'I'm not going on a pleasure trip, this is strictly business.' His voice had darkened, disapproval threading his tones. Clearly he didn't want her company, but Claire had a feeling this would be her very last chance to see him alone and there were so many things she wanted to explain, so many things that she wanted him to understand.

She raised her head, forcing herself to meet his eyes. 'I wouldn't be a nuisance, honestly,' she persisted quietly.

She saw his face tighten. She heard him sigh. But then he nodded faintly. 'Be ready in thirty minutes. I shan't wait.'

Claire left the room the moment he gave his grudging acceptance, her cheeks still flushed with embarrassed colour. She was behaving badly. She didn't recognise herself. She knew Jake didn't want her company but she had put him in a position from which it was impossible to refuse. She knew she ought to be ashamed of herself, but she also knew that she wasn't. She wanted to be with Jake and at this moment that was her only consideration.

CHAPTER EIGHT

SHE was ready well within the thirty minutes that Jake had specified, her peasant costume abandoned carelessly on the bed, a simple cream-and-brown skirt and blouse, topped by a stylish blue raincoat, replacing it. She ran down the back stairs, anxious not to give Jake any reason for leaving her. But he hadn't arrived, she realised as she walked slowly out on to the pebbled courtyard, there was no sign of either Jake or his car. She stood and waited under the stone canopy outside the back door, squinting up at the increasingly heavy clouds, wondering what could have possessed her to force her company on Jake as she had done. She could guess exactly what he must be thinking. Her behaviour this morning had no doubt confirmed all his most damning suspicions about her.

She had almost persuaded herself to walk back into the house and allow him to leave without her when the door flew open behind her. She turned slowly, watching, her green eyes wide, her ridiculous heartbeats pounding away at an alarming rate. True to his words he had changed and he looked gorgeous, his pale grey suit giving him an air of cool elegance, a stark contrast to his brooding, dark good looks.

And they were certainly brooding, Claire realised. He barely glanced her way, staring instead at the large drops of rain, falling steadily now beyond the sheltered doorway.

'What bloody weather!' As words of greeting they were hardly reassuring and Claire stared at him, wondering yet again why she had come, what she had hoped to gain? Because it was too late to back out now. That would only make her look more ridiculous.

She hoped that once they were in the car his black

131

mood would lift a little, but it seemed that he was
determined to show her just how unwelcome she was
without actually putting his feelings into words. She
talked a little at first about safe, neutral subjects, but
his replies were so monosyllabic that in the end she just
gave up and sat in silence as intense as his own, her eyes
on the rain lashing wildly against the windscreen and
the wet road snaking ahead. She knew she'd brought
this on herself, but that knowledge didn't ease her
misery in any way. Her relationship with Jake seemed
to be one long uphill struggle, each time she thought
she'd made some progress, something came along and
knocked her to the bottom of the ladder again. Was it
worth it? she wondered. Here they were, locked in the
intimacy of his small car and she might as well have
been invisible. She had hoped that maybe he was still
attracted to her a little, but it seemed that she'd misread
all the signs. He quite clearly didn't give a damn.

She sank lower into her seat, lost in the misery of her
own thoughts and only slowly did it dawn on her that
the discomfort in her stomach was not a product of
emotional distress. Quite simply she felt sick. The
narrow roads with their tight Z-bends, the speed at
which they were travelling, combined with her empty
stomach had all taken their toll. She was mortified but
she hung on grimly, determined not to succumb to her
physical weakness, groaning inwardly as the powerful
car surged around yet another tight bend, her eyes
searching desperately for a landmark which would
signal their approach to Penzance. But all she could see
were trees and fields whipping past the windows, their
burgeoning green blurred and softened by the pouring
rain.

Her attention was drawn back to the front
windscreen as Jake eased his foot from the accelerator
slightly. A lorry loaded with sheep had loomed
suddenly out of the rain in front of them and the
powerful car was compelled to slow to a crawl. But then
with a quick thrust on the accelerator they were past.

The cold sweat prickled Claire's brow and down her spine. She felt terrible. But even then she might still have managed to maintain her shaky façade if at that moment the car had not swung quickly around another tight corner. She couldn't repress a groan, her hand flying to her lips.

Jake's head jerked around. He took one look at her ashen face, cursing softly as he checked the driving mirror and stood sharply on his brakes, swinging the car off the road and into the narrow, churned-up opening leading to a field gate.

Claire had loosened her seat belt and pushed open the door even before the movement had stopped, her high heels sinking into the wet ground as she staggered towards the gate. The air was cool and damp and she sucked it into her lungs gratefully, sagging against the gate, her hair darkened to dull bronze by the falling rain.

She knew Jake had followed her out of the car. She could hear him breathing behind her, but she ignored him completely, staring blindly into the empty field, the pent up fury inside threatening to rise up and choke her. She didn't understand him. She didn't know what he wanted from her. One minute he was all seductive charm and the next, those cold blue eyes were spitting icy sparks at her. Well she just didn't want to know any longer. She was furious with him but even more furious with herself, she realised with a tiny inward groan of despair. It ought to be easy, putting him out of her mind, but it wasn't going to be, in fact it would be impossible and the knowledge made her turn on him, spitting like a cat when he put out a tentative hand and touched her shoulder. 'Are you okay?' he asked.

Claire swayed against the gate, angry words choking in her throat, but Jake still seemed unaware of the fury he had unleashed.

'Are you okay?' he asked again. He sighed, shaking his head, concern in his tones. 'I'm sorry, I didn't know you were subject to car sickness. I feel like a brute. I drove far too quickly under the circumstances.' He was smiling gently down at her, apparently attributing her pale cheeks and trembling lips to purely physical symptoms. 'I really am very sorry.'

This was too much for Claire and she glared at him, her green eyes suspiciously bright. 'You're sorry!' she cried, damp tendrils of hair tumbling wildly around her cheeks. 'I'm the one that's sorry, believe me! I'm sorry I ever came to the audition for *Wrecker's Bride*. I'm sorry I was ever offered a part in your bloody film! But above all I'm sorry that I ever met you!' The words came out in one, wild, angry rush, pain and fury blazing simultaneously in her eyes. It was true, she thought angrily. She did wish she had never met him. He was a constant, tormenting thorn in her flesh, and she wanted him out.

It was Jake's turn to look at her as though he couldn't quite believe his ears, his blue eyes narrowed in amazement, fingers tightening painfully on her shoulders. 'If you've quite finished perhaps you'd like to listen to me for a moment,' he bit out coolly.

Claire stared at him with tormented, angry eyes. 'I wouldn't! No, I wouldn't!' she shouted bitterly. 'I'm through listening to you! All you do is put me down. I know just exactly what you think of me, you've made it painfully obvious. I should never have come today. I was a fool!' Claire couldn't go on. She was shaking with emotion and she dropped her head to hide the tears she knew were filling her eyes.

'We're both fools, I would agree with you there,' he stated abruptly. 'Standing about in the pouring rain like this.' He took her resisting elbow in a steely grip and began to pull her towards the car, but she dug in her heels, trying to hang back and he glared at her, his chin jutting angrily. 'You're soaked to the skin. You'll catch pneumonia. Is that what you want, you little fool?'

Claire shot him a bitter glance. 'Do you care? Do you really care?'

His mouth tightened. 'Yes I care!' He opened the

passenger door. 'Now, do you get into this car under your own steam, or do I throw you in bodily?'

Claire slid in, her mouth sulky, deliberately staring straight ahead as he walked around the car and climbed in beside her. 'Now, I suggest that you take off that damp coat, quieten down a little and we'll make some attempt to talk sensibly to each other for a change,' he said calmly.

Claire felt sick, she was wet, her damp clothes sticking to her and she'd had about as much as she could take. She turned to face him, her green eyes flashing angrily. 'Don't patronise me, Jake!' she yelled. 'Just don't do it! As I said before, I know exactly what you think of me.' Unshed tears were tightening her chest and she choked back a sob. 'It seems there's nothing I can do to change your opinion, so just take me into Penzance and leave me there. I won't trouble you again. I'll ring Mike, he won't be working this afternoon, he'll come to collect me.'

The effect of Claire's words was electric. Jake's fingers shot out and imprisoned her nape in a grip of steel, his blue eyes suddenly blazing down at her. 'Like hell he will! You're going nowhere with Mike Brent.' His fingers tightened. 'Do you hear me? If we go into Penzance then I'm the one who will bring you home.'

Claire tried to twist her neck out of his grip but couldn't. This had happened to her before. It was getting to be a habit with him and she didn't like it. 'You're hurting me, Jake. Let me go,' she moaned. She hardly knew what she was saying now. Jake was leaning over her, the hard length of his body touching hers, his warm breath on her cheek, his eyes a blue flame, melting her anger. 'Let me go. You don't want me.'

She was still trying to twist away and he laughed suddenly so that she stopped and stared at him. 'I don't want you!' He repeated her words his voice heavy with irony. 'Dear God, Claire, I don't know whether to laugh or cry. If only you knew.'

He had released his hold on her nape but Claire

didn't move, she simply sat frozen to the spot as his hand slid to her jaw, his fingers probing her soft skin, every brief touch a caress. He was watching her intently, his burning eyes fixed on her softly parted lips. 'I do want you, Claire,' he murmured now. 'You've been under my skin since the very first day we met.'

Claire's heart was beating so quickly she could hardly breathe. This couldn't be happening to her. She didn't believe it. But she had to believe it. Jake was still smiling down into her eyes, his fingers gently stroking her cheek, his thumb parting her lips, his head moving closer and closer so that Claire began to tremble wildly and couldn't stop.

His mouth was firm, moving slowly, sensuously over her lips. She ought to be fighting him, she tried to fight him, her hands moving to push him away and then sliding on as though she had no control over them, slipping around his neck, her fingers tangling in his hair, her whole body arching towards him. His kiss lengthened and deepened and she was on fire, throbbing, tiny flames licking along her veins so that she could think of nothing but the liquid, melting sensations he was arousing inside her.

His hands were moving slowly over her body now and she moaned softly, her eyes tightly closed, pressing herself against him in mindless provocation.

'Claire, darling,' he groaned thickly. 'I'm going crazy . . .'

He was still kissing her, touching her and she was letting him, she had no resistance. I'm the one who must be crazy, she thought. I love Jake! All the time I was telling myself I hated him it wasn't true. She was trembling now, love and desire, desire and love intermingled, tangling her thoughts and emotions as she writhed beneath his exploring hands, gasping with pleasure as his mouth followed the trail his hands had made on her creamy skin.

He raised his head at last, his blue eyes agonised. 'God, Claire, I want you!' He was breathing hard and fast, staring down at her naked breasts as though he never wanted to take his eyes off her. He moved his head slowly from side to side. 'I want you . . . I want to make love to you!' This last was a hoarse cry and Claire stared at him, her expression as dazed as his own, her soft mouth bruised from the hungry possession of his long kisses.

What had happened to her? What had happened to the cool, controlled girl she once used to be? She had disappeared for ever, she realised. Burnt up in the fever of Jake's lovemaking. She was still watching him. There was passion, hunger, desire in his eyes—if there was love she couldn't see it. But she realised that she no longer cared, her own feelings were too strong. With a tiny cry she reached out for him again, pulling his dark head back towards her, his mouth moving hungrily over her lips, his hands searching, stroking, restlessly exploring her soft, pliant body until she cried aloud, 'Jake, love me please . . .'

In that moment she didn't care that they were at the side of a public highway. The vehicles rumbling past the misted windows were shadows. She and Jake were in a small, private world. He was her only reality, and yet it was her own pleading words that broke the spell surrounding them.

His head jerked up the moment she'd spoken. His muttered, 'Oh God!' a tortured exclamation as he pulled away from her, covering his eyes with a hand that was not quite steady. 'I must be going out of my mind,' he muttered hoarsely.

Claire shivered, wrapping the ends of her shirt around her shaking body. She felt bereft. She had been floating on a hazy cloud of sensual feeling and now she had come back down to earth with a painful bump, still unsure what had happened, watching Jake with wide green eyes.

He was breathing roughly, through half-closed lips. 'I'm sorry, Claire,' he muttered.

'Why Jake? Why are you doing this?' she demanded.

She was still too dazed to sort out any coherent thoughts from the tangled mess that was her brain. She only knew that Jake had seemed as passionately involved as she was herself and now he was sitting as far away from her as possible, an expression of self-loathing written all over his taut features.

He turned to her, not touching her, but watching with shadowed eyes as her shaking fingers fumbled, trying to fasten the buttons of her blouse. 'I want to touch you,' he told her huskily, 'I want to make love to you. I can't remember when I've wanted anything so much. But I have no right to do so.'

Claire's fingers slowed, as her muzzy brain tried to grasp his meaning. 'If it's because you saw Mike in my room, you don't need to worry. He came to wait for me, that's all. Nothing happened, nothing ever has. He's a friend . . .'

He shook his head, holding her eyes with a burning blue gaze. 'For the sake of my sanity I have to believe that's true,' he murmured. 'The thought of him touching you, making love to you has been driving me crazy these last few weeks. I was so insane with jealousy when I saw him in your room . . . on your bed, that I just couldn't think straight. I realised later,' he smiled, a faint, self-derisive tilt of his firm mouth, 'when I'd calmed down a bit, that I'd probably put two and two together and made five.' He touched her cheek gently. 'Jumping to conclusions about you seems to be something that I'm very good at.'

Claire knew she was staring at him with her heart in her eyes, but she was overflowing with emotion, it was impossible to hide it.

He was still talking, grasping her hands, holding them tightly. 'It's Marianne,' he told her quickly. 'She thinks that she's in love with me.'

'But Jake . . .' Claire tried to interrupt but he wouldn't let her.

'Let me finish, Claire,' he murmured, covering her mouth witth his hand. 'I want you to understand what's happening.' He sighed heavily now. 'I knew how Marianne felt when I offered her the part, so you could say that I've brought this on my own head. But I thought I could handle it.' He paused, his eyes dark blue pools in which Claire was slowly sinking. 'That was until you came on the scene.'

'Jake I . . .' Claire wanted to say that she didn't care about Marianne. She didn't care about the past. In fact she'd completely forgotten Marianne's existence until this moment.

But Jake shook his head again. 'No, let me finish. God knows, it's hard enough.' He turned abruptly, facing out of the windscreen, his jaw taut, apparently completely absorbed by the dripping landscape beyond the window. 'Marianne went wild, crazy, when she saw me bringing you home from the village that night,' he continued quietly. 'She threatened to walk out on the film, break her contract. I knew then that this had to stop.' He looked down at his hands on the wheel, his smile wry. 'In a way it was almost a relief when I found Brent in your room. I doubt if I could have kept away from you otherwise.'

Claire's voice was very quiet. 'Is that why Marianne was so horrible to me today?' she asked.

He nodded. 'I'm sorry about that, Claire. I wanted to tear a strip off her, but I couldn't. I'm walking a knife edge. She heard about that episode on the cliff top.' He pulled a face, half-laughing, half self-derisive. 'I think the way I kissed you must have painted a pretty explicit picture for everyone. I had one hell of a job calming her down afterwards.'

Claire sat very still, her head bent, her vivid hair hiding her face. No wonder she'd been confused. No wonder she hadn't been able to fathom Jake's motives. He'd been attracted to her all the time, it had been Marianne holding him back. She heard him move. But she kept her head down. Her face was too expressive, it showed too much.

'There's something else I ought to tell you.' He was

watching her, she could feel his eyes on her bent head. 'Marianne and I have known each other for years.' He paused and she sensed his shrug. 'We used to be lovers. We were together for a long time, until quite recently in fact. But we were always working at opposite ends of the globe and we simply drifted apart. I thought the decision to separate, go our own way, was mutual, but it seems I was mistaken.' He kept on talking, his voice quiet and without emotion and Claire listened, her hands clenched tightly in her lap. 'That's another reason I've tried to stay away from you. Sometimes I feel I'd like to strangle Marianne.' He gave a short laugh. 'She can be a bitch. But I am fond of her still. We had some good times together and I don't want to hurt her any more than I have to.'

'So that's it then. Thank you for explaining.' Claire tried to say all that in a cool little voice, but failed miserably. Jake was attracted to her, but not enough it seemed. Marianne still held all the cards, she was still more important to him.

Jake sighed, raking a hand through his already dishevelled hair. 'For God's sake, Claire, what else can I do?'

'Nothing of course,' she answered tightly.

'Once the film is finished I shall be free to do as I please. I planned to take a long holiday,' he murmured. 'I was hoping you'd let me see something of you then?'

Claire tried to ignore the pleading note in his voice. She wouldn't allow herself to hope. He was an attractive, very sexy man. Other women beside herself and Marianne would find him so. A lot could happen in the next two months. Even if Marianne didn't wear his resistance down someone else might manage to do so. She wanted him now! Not in two months' time.

He had been watching her and now his fingers curved around her chin, lifting it until he could see her face. 'Do you think I want it to be like this?' he sighed. He waited for her to answer and when she remained stubbornly silent, he leaned forward, claiming her mouth with a sudden, hungry kiss, his lips moving with brief, but violent passion over her own. When he released her he was breathing hard, a dark flush staining his cheeks and Claire stared at him helplessly, her mouth trembling.

'I want you, Claire,' he jerked out hoarsely. 'But I can't ask you to indulge in some little hole-in-the-corner affair. Hell, if you're mine I want to be able to shout it to the world.' His eyes moved over her slowly, hungrily, the passion in their depths leaving Claire in no doubt that he meant what he said.

She put out her hand and touched his cheek, her fingers very gentle. 'I want you too,' she told him honestly. Perhaps she was a fool. Perhaps she ought to have been playing hard to get, but she couldn't let him go, not now, when she knew that she loved him. If there was a chance of happiness with Jake she was going to take it and she refused to let her stupid pride stand in the way.

'I want to spend time with you now,' she continued softly. 'Who knows what will have happened by the end of filming?' She held his eyes, her own very warm, a soft glowing green. 'I would be discreet, I promise. I can't pretend to like Marianne but I would try not to upset her. But it's got to be your decision, Jake.'

She held her breath, waiting, watching his face, seeing his thoughts and emotions reflected on it.

'Claire, darling,' he spoke at last, his voice husky with emotion. 'You're right, I can't wait. I can't keep away from you. You're too darned tempting.'

He jerked her back into his arms, his kiss taking her breath away. She had won, Claire realised, but her happiness was far from perfect. Take what you want and pay for it were the words that flashed across her brain. She loved Jake and she wanted him, but she wondered just how high the payment was going to be.

CHAPTER NINE

CLAIRE stretched lazily, her sun-warmed body completely relaxed, arms clasped behind her head, eyes half-closed, her drowsy gaze fixed on the gleaming white sails of a yacht creaming along on the vivid blue sea. For days now the weather had been perfect, blue skies, hot sunshine, the merest whisper of breeze stirring the ancient oaks behind the house. She sighed as a skylark began to sing somewhere in the blue distance, its melody so beautiful that it almost hurt to listen. The bird song had pierced her mood, making her suddenly restless so that she threw herself on to her stomach, the fragrance of warm, crushed grass rising from beneath her as she moved.

She ought to be idyllically happy. She was young and in love. She sighed again, screwing up her eyes against the sun. Unfortunately life was never quite so simple. At the moment hers was a bit like a beautiful rosy apple, perfect on the outside but with a nasty little worm niggling away at the core and spoiling all that perfection.

And Jake had undoubtedly become the core of her world during the last few weeks. There was scarcely a moment of the day when she wasn't thinking about him, whatever she did he was present in her mind. She only had to close her eyes and she could see him. She did that now, her pale lids covering the vivid green, and there he was, his dark, handsome image a permanent imprint on her retina.

She jerked her eyes open and sat up abruptly, her gaze fixed on the distant horizon. Sometimes these days she really wondered if she was going slightly crazy. She didn't recognise herself any longer. She seemed to be a weak stranger without a will of her own, no longer in charge of her own destiny. Her life completely out of control like a satellite spinning crazily, way off its orbit.

She loved Jake more with every passing day. And desire certainly hadn't faded, not for either of them. But it was no longer enough. She had become possessive, greedy, and she wanted everything. They talked, but afterwards Claire would realise that he had told her nothing. He knew everything there was to know about her but she knew no more about him than she did at their first meeting. He never talked about his family or his past. He was an enigma and Claire was afraid, terrified of her own jealousy, terrified of the ease with which he could hurt her.

Claire's thoughts were too disturbing and she couldn't sit still any longer, so she pushed herself to her feet, brushing the grass from her cotton skirt with restless fingers, her steps automatically following the faint path leading towards the manor, her thoughts still in the same well-worn groove.

Jake desired her, she knew that was true. She was a fever in his blood, he told her, and maybe that's all she was. Some day the fever would disappear and she would be left with nothing but painful memories. She slowed, shivering a little, although the sun was as warm as ever on her back. Sometimes she feared that he still cared more for Marianne than he did for her. At dinner they still sat together, talking, Jake's dark head close to Marianne's fair one, and Claire couldn't bear to watch. Jealousy was a fierce, searing pain in her breast whenever she saw them together. She wanted to scream at them, lash out and make them suffer as she was doing. But she did nothing. She hadn't even told Jake how she felt. Her pride had been trampled in the dust recently but she had too much for that. He had never promised her anything and she certainly wasn't going to beg. And secretly she was still afraid that if she made demands upon him it would destroy the faint, delicate threads which bound them together.

Later that same day Jake asked Claire to spend a

weekend away with him. They had been filming in the garden and he stopped her before she went to her room.

'I want to talk to you, Claire,' he murmured, his head bent, speaking low, his blue eyes flicking over her pale shoulders with a disturbingly intent gaze. She was still wearing her peasant costume, the white blouse cut low, and clearly Jake appreciated the fact. 'Don't change, Claire. Wait for me in the office. I shan't be long.'

Claire did as she was told, her heart thumping loudly as she walked down the corridor towards the office. Maybe Jake didn't share very much of himself with her, but fool that she was she needed everything that he was prepared to give. He entered the office only a couple of minutes after she did and he strode towards her, his blue eyes blazing, the message in their depths unmistakable.

Claire stood and trembled under that hungry gaze. She wanted him. She loved him. It was at once a pain and a pleasure as his arms slid around her, pulling her close against his hard length, his mouth moving over her closed lids, over her cheekbones, parting her lips with increasing urgency. Claire was drowning in desire, her mind empty of everything but Jake. She pressed herself against him feverishly, her skin hot, her eyes tight shut, her expression dazed, moaning softly as his lips burned the soft white skin of her bared breast, hardly knowing that it was her own voice that she heard.

'You're beautiful . . . so beautiful,' Jake breathed.

Claire forced her heavy lids to open. He was staring at her, his blue eyes flaring with passion. 'I can't go on like this. I want you. I'm going crazy for you.' His voice was hoarse, husky and Claire gazed at him wordlessly. She wanted him, too. She loved him. She wanted to please him. But she stayed silent and he spoke again, not hearing, not understanding.

'I need you, Claire. I need you so much. Will you come away with me?' he breathed. As he spoke his hand moved, cupping her breast so that she groaned aloud.

'You want me too,' he whispered. 'Admit it. We could go somewhere quiet where no one knows us. Please darling . . .'

His husky, sensual voice conjured up pleasures which Claire could only dream about. She knew she ought to refuse. This would only bring her pain. Jake wanted her body . . . he didn't love her. But even while her brain was shaping these sensible thoughts her soft voice was saying, 'Yes . . . yes, whenever you like.'

'It can't be this weekend, I have to go to London,' he breathed against her forehead. Claire could feel him trembling but she didn't try to fool herself, it was passion not love that was weakening his body.

'I'll make the arrangements for the weekend after that,' he was saying softly. 'My darling, I can hardly wait.'

Claire knew her behaviour was stupid, but she could hardly wait either. She'd been horrified when Alan Crosby had suggested she become his mistress, but here she was agreeing to jump into bed with Jake the moment he asked her. Love had turned her mind into a crazy mess, but she still spent the next few days in a fever of anticipation, elation and depression fighting for the upper hand in her brain.

Jake was busier than ever. He and the producer spending long hours peering at the rushes, production being hurried along at a tremendous pace. She knew they were pleased with the results so far. Everyone on the team was pleased. Even Marianne had a smile on her face, except when she turned her eyes on Claire. Then they glittered with malice, hard blue pebbles which told Claire that whoever else she and Jake were fooling, Marianne guessed that something was going on between them.

But Marianne still carried on filming. She didn't break her contract. She didn't cause any waves. She even worked opposite Claire without causing any further difficulties. But her constant, shadowy presence troubled Claire, increasing her uncertainty about Jake.

What did he really feel for Marianne? Did he still care for her? Did he still love her? Was she, Claire, a temporary passion, soon to be burned out? As usual when Jake fitted into the picture there were questions and no apparent way to discover satisfactory answers.

Jake's visit to London was to go ahead as planned. He was aiming to leave on the Friday afternoon and Claire only saw him briefly before he went, a snatched, frantic ten minutes of urgent caresses which left them both weak and trembling and longing for more. Claire longed for their brief, hurried meetings and yet she had come to hate them too. She hated the secrecy. It fed her jealousy. She wanted her relationship with Jake to be out in the open. Dark suspicions had grown in her mind, only exposure to the light and fresh air would drive them away.

By five o'clock on Friday both Jake and the producer had departed. Claire changed out of her costume quickly, showered and dressed again in a simple striped cotton frock. She had seen Mike briefly at lunchtime and he had asked her to meet him before he returned to the village so she sped down the stairs and out into the courtyard wondering what he wanted to say to her. In fact she felt guilty about Mike. She'd been avoiding him deliberately recently, and she knew he was hurt. This was simply another measure of the way Jake had taken over her life. Mike's friendship was important to her, but she knew Jake still harboured suspicions about their relationship so she'd started to avoid Mike. It was crazy behaviour. But Claire had stopped trying to fight it because she knew she wouldn't win.

Mike was waiting for her beside his car, lounging against the bonnet, hands in pockets, face upturned, his eyes half-shut, apparently drowsing in the late afternoon sunshine. But he turned as he heard Claire's feet crunching over the gravel, his smile as warm as ever. And guilt struck Claire a deeper wound. She had been unfriendly but it seemed he bore her no grudge. Anger would have been easier to face, Claire thought as she drew nearer.

'Hello, my lovely. Long time no see.' His voice was deliberately light but Claire sensed the unspoken question. She sighed, if only she could tell him the truth.

'Hello, Mike,' she murmured. It was no use, she had to say something. She couldn't let Mike think she had suddenly gone off him, without reason. She met his eyes, her own gaze troubled. 'I'm sorry, Mike, this is not how I want it to be. I know I've been unfriendly.' She stopped, her head bent, tracing a path in the pebbles with her toe. 'I feel mean, but I'm sorry, I can't explain.' Her words hardly made the grade, either as an apology or an explanation but Mike seemed to understand.

'It's okay, love, don't worry,' he said. His brown eyes were warm and shrewd, still smiling at her. 'Is it difficult for you to talk now? Have I put my foot in it by asking you to meet me?'

'It's fine, honestly,' Claire was quick to reassure him.

'I just wanted to warn you. Alan's on his way down. He called in to see Joan yesterday and offered her a lift. And I'm afraid he's coming to see you, Claire.'

He fell silent and Claire stared at him blank-faced, until slowly the meaning of his words sank in, her cheeks paling until they were as white as a sheet. This couldn't be happening to her, it just couldn't. She thought Alan Crosby had vanished from her life for good, but it seemed he hadn't, and true to form he had chosen the very worst possible moment to reappear.

'I don't understand, I just don't understand.' She faced Mike, her eyes wide and shocked. 'Why is he coming, Mike? It's over between us! I don't want him here!' He could ruin everything. Jake would never understand.

Mike was sympathetic but unable to give her any reassurance. 'I'm sorry, Claire. I knew you wouldn't want to see him. Joan refused his offer at first, but,' he shrugged, 'Alan said he was coming anyway. Apparently he invited Lynn as well but she was working this weekend.'

Claire stared at the ground, biting her lip, her mind miles away from the words she was saying. 'Yes, she wrote and told me she was flying to Jersey. She's been offered some catalogue work and they're filming on the island,' she murmured absently. And then she raised her head, her eyes bright, feverish with anxiety. 'Oh Mike, what am I going to do? I can't see him. But knowing Alan he just won't take no for an answer. Goodness knows I've said it to him often enough in the past.'

If Jake discovered that Alan had visited her while he was in London Claire knew he would think the worst. He would suspect that she had planned the visit to coincide with his absence. Too many things had happened in the past, he would never believe that she was entirely innocent.

Mike sighed now, running a hand through his dark hair. 'I don't know what to suggest. I'll try to keep him away, Claire, but I can't promise anything. Wouldn't it be easier to see him and give him the hard word? Joan and I could come along and lend some moral support.'

Claire turned, her eyes on the distant blue of sea and sky. 'You don't understand. It's not that simple.' Her voice was shaky, anxiety gnawing away in the pit of her stomach. She would have to tell him about Jake, she realised. It was the only way. Maybe he would be able to think of a solution once he knew the truth. She began to talk and Mike listened, his dark eyes fixed intently on her face.

'So you see,' she finished at last. 'If Alan comes now when Jake's away, he will think I've arranged the visit deliberately.'

She saw Mike's expression and sighed. It was true, Jake was far from being trusting. But she had behaved like an appalling little tart at their first meeting. No wonder his suspicions were so easily aroused. She said this to Mike and he shook his head, his dark eyes sceptical.

'The man's a fool,' he told Claire quietly. 'If he knows anything about you at all he must realise that you're just not that kind of woman.'

'He's had reason,' Claire murmured. She knew Mike was genuinely concerned about her and she was grateful, but right now she was only interested in avoiding Alan's visit. She couldn't think of anything else. 'I don't want to spoil Joan's visit,' she continued quietly. 'I know how much you must be looking forward to seeing her again. But please, if you can, stop Alan from coming here to see me. If Marianne even gets a faint hint of his visit you can be sure that Jake will be the first to know.'

'I'll do my best, Claire. But honestly, I think you're over-dramatising Svenson's reaction.'

Claire shook her head and sighed. She would have liked to agree with him, but she knew Jake, she knew just how suspicious he could be. But there was no point in trying to explain to Mike. He was such a kind, straightforward person himself that he would never understand the convoluted workings of Jake Svenson's mind. Claire wasn't sure that she understood herself, but she did know that she loved him and didn't want to lose him.

'Is Joan staying until Monday?' she asked now, deliberately changing the subject and Mike took the hint and began to talk of other things.

He left soon afterwards, ringing her later to say that Alan and Joan had arrived, and that Alan was still determined to see her again. 'I've explained to him that it's over between you but he seems to think that you only need to talk to each other and everything will be okay. I've done my best love, but honestly, he just won't listen.'

Claire sighed, biting her lip, her eyes fixed unseeingly on the wooden panelled wall in front of her. She knew the feeling. Alan never listened to anything that she said, either. There was no help for it, she would obviously have to see him herself and try to make him understand. And pray that Jake didn't hear about it.

She was quiet for so long that Mike began to talk again, his voice low and apologetic. 'I said I would arrange for us all to collect you at ten-thirty tomorrow. I thought if Joan and I came too it would maybe provide some necessary camouflage.'

Claire agreed to his suggestion gratefully and they made the arrangements before she returned to her room to change for dinner. It was a silent meal, with only a dozen members of the company present, but Marianne was there and it was difficult for Claire to avoid her eyes. Marianne seemed to watch her and Claire had the ridiculous feeling that the other woman could see into her brain and knew exactly what was going to happen tomorrow. It was a relief when dinner was over and she could finally escape to her room.

Sleep came at last and she woke to another bright morning, the sky a perfect blue, birds singing, the scent of early summer drifting through her open window. Her spirits began to rise as soon as she drew back the curtains. It was hard to be gloomy on a morning like this. She showered and dressed quickly, donning an old pair of jeans and a long-sleeved cotton shirt. It was obviously going to be a warm day but she was determined not to encourage Alan's pretensions with even the faintest trace of bare flesh.

The dining room was almost empty when she entered, everyone either having a lie-in or had eaten earlier in order to make the best of the free weekend. It suited Claire, she didn't want a large audience when Alan arrived. She ate quickly, and after returning to her room to wash her hands and collect her shoulder bag she went to wait for her visitors outside, wandering around the front garden, enjoying the sounds and the scents of the morning, one eye on the road.

She saw the MG as it turned the sharp corner at the top of the hill and walked slowly to meet it, sighing, all her pleasure in the beautiful morning vanishing instantly. They were close enough for her to recognise the passengers now, and her heart sank as she saw Alan in the back seat. She'd still been hoping that he wouldn't come, she realised. But there he was, looking as sure of himself as ever.

Claire turned her head away deliberately and waved to Joan, smiling warmly. It was wonderful to see her again. If only Alan hadn't appeared she knew she would have enjoyed a day spent in Joan and Mike's cheerful company. The car crunched to a halt beside her, Claire still avoiding Alan's eye. The man was an appalling nuisance, she decided. She no longer cared whether she hurt him or not.

Joan had opened her door and was clambering out. 'Hi Claire! How does it feel to be one of the rich and famous?' she cried. Joan was small and dark and slightly overweight, with a very pale, plain little face, but when she smiled as she was smiling now, she seemed to be lit from within. Claire had never met anyone who could resist that smile. At school Joan had taken part in one hilarious escapade after another, but with the help of her smile had managed to extricate not only herself, but everyone else, from the painful consequences.

'I'm working too hard to notice,' Claire said now with a laugh.

'So Mike tells me.' Joan's teasing eyes were on her husband now. 'Although I was beginning to think it was just a fairy story.'

'Scout's honour, Joan, we're working like slaves.'

Joan pulled a face at her husband and Claire watched, smiling, enjoying their banter and wishing that her own relationship with Jake was founded on such a firm bedrock of mutual trust. She knew Alan had climbed out of the car behind her but she kept her back firmly turned towards him. Maybe she ought not to have been surprised when his arm closed around her waist, but she was. It had never entered her head that he would try to touch her. The man was egotistical and self-opinionated with a skin like a rhinoceros, she decided as she turned angrily to face him, struggling furiously to free herself. He held on tight. Not only that, but one hand slid into her hair, gripping her head,

holding her firmly, so that she couldn't escape the
hungry kiss he planted on her mouth.

She tried to jerk away, pushing her hands against his
chest, revolted by the intimate way his lips moved over
her own. There was absolute silence from Joan and
Mike. She knew they must be as stunned as she was
herself. The kiss went on and on. She hated it. She
hated him and when he released her at last, breathing
hard, his face flushed, she raised her hand intending to
inflict a stinging rebuke on that arrogant cheek. But the
movement was never carried through. Her arm
dropped, lifeless to her side, her bruised mouth hanging
open in shock and dismay.

Marianne had just walked out of the house, the
housekeeper's golden-haired spaniel at her heels, and
she had seen that kiss, triumph written all over her face
as she stared mockingly across the courtyard at Claire.
She knew what Jake was like. She knew he would be
furious with Claire. He would never forgive her, Claire
realised. He would never understand. Alan's visit would
have been difficult enough to explain away, but the kiss
would be impossible.

Claire knew Mike was talking to her, but she couldn't
absorb the words. Her brain was still too occupied with
the memory of Marianne's expression as she had turned
away and walked into the garden. He took her arm
now, urging her towards the car and she followed on
shaky legs. There was no point in avoiding Alan's
company at this stage. The damage was done. And she
certainly didn't want to go back into the house and risk
meeting Marianne again.

Mike drove them back to the village, the hood down,
Claire's bronze-red curls whipping around her face. Alan
still seemed not to understand his position and when he
reached for her again, she turned on him, her green eyes
spitting flames, her hoarse, angry voice telling him in no
uncertain terms exactly what she thought of him.

'And I never want to see you again as long as I live,'
she finished, her chin up, her eyes flashing angrily.

His face paled and he sank back in his seat without a word. Claire could see that he was furious, but as Joan and Mike were silent, unwilling spectators she was spared one of his furious outbursts. He went straight to his room when they reached the hotel and Claire didn't see him again. She had intended to return to the manor immediately, but Joan pressed her so anxiously to spend the rest of the day with them, that in the end she gave in. Maybe it was cowardly of her. She knew they must be longing to spend some time alone together, but the thought of facing Marianne across the dinner table was the deciding factor. She couldn't do it. Marianne would be triumphant. Claire didn't need a crystal ball to know that she would run to Jake with her story the moment he arrived. Only Claire intended to get there first, before Marianne had a chance to spread her poison.

She rose early on Sunday morning. She had woken at first light, roused by the dawn chorus and had been unable to get back to sleep again, her body rigid under the covers, her eyes wide open staring at the ceiling as she turned over and over in her mind the words she planned to say to Jake when she returned. The day was hot and sunny again, she realised when she finally climbed out of bed, but this morning there was a breeze blowing from the sea, the waves rushing into the bay below the house, crashing with reverberating force against the rocks.

After breakfast she decided to leave Ardwennan for a while and go for a walk. Jake wasn't due back until around six and if she haunted the house and its vicinity she knew she would be bound to bump into Marianne. And that she did not want. So she donned an old pair of sturdy shoes, threw a cardigan around her shoulders and set off to walk along the cliff tops. The air was like wine. Claire could have been all alone in a world of sea and sky and for a brief time she forgot her worries, walking for miles along the turf.

It was almost four o'clock when she returned. The beauty and tranquillity of the day had had a soothing effect on her fears. Surely if Jake cared for her at all he would give her the benefit of the doubt. Alan's arrival looked damning in itself, but once he listened to her explanation he would surely understand. Suddenly she felt infinitely more optimistic. There was even a spring in her step as she climbed the stairs to her room. She washed her face and hands quickly and tidied her hair. There was always an afternoon tea set out in the dining room at this time, usually she didn't bother but today she had missed her lunch and she was ravenous. She hurried downstairs, walking straight into the room through the half-opened door, coming to an abrupt halt as she saw the room's sole occupant.

Marianne was smiling at her mockingly, the glowing scarlet of her dress proclaiming her triumph without her needing any words. Claire knew she had paled. She knew she was trembling. But it was too late to escape. She took an unsteady breath and forced her legs in the direction of the sideboard where the sandwiches and cakes had been arranged. She wouldn't allow Marianne to drive her away. She studied the laden plates determinedly, choosing from the delicate sandwiches and tiny, iced buns at random, before walking back to the table and setting her plate down as far away from Marianne as possible.

The silence grew steadily as Claire forced herself to eat and Claire's tension grew with it so that every small sound—the occasional scrape of a knife on the flower-patterned china or the rattle of a cup in its saucer seemed an intolerable intrusion, tearing at her nerves. It was almost a relief when Marianne spoke at last. Claire raised her head to listen, her chin up, her green eyes masking her fear.

'You think you've been so clever, don't you?' Marianne was still smiling, but her blue eyes stabbed at Claire like knives. 'Did you really believe that I couldn't see what was going on under my nose?' she asked with a soft, contemptuous laugh. 'Of course I saw, I saw very clearly. You pursued Jake. You flaunted sex at him.

You were a walking invitation.' Her voice had risen, bright flags of colour burning in her cheeks. 'You thought you could win, didn't you? But believe me Jake's not such a fool. He's using you, Claire Grant and it will cost him nothing to discard you!'

Marianne's words were getting to Claire. It took an increasing effort to hold up her head and meet the other woman's eyes without flinching, as her taunting voice played upon fears which Claire had barely acknowledged that she harboured until this moment. Did Jake not care for her at all? Was she just a sexy body to him and nothing more?

She forced her voice to work at last. 'I didn't pursue Jake,' she insisted huskily. 'It was something that happened to both of us. It was a mutual attraction.'

Marianne was laughing. 'Really, my dear, how naive you are. Jake's been using you. You made it perfectly clear that you were available and he quite simply took what you offered.'

'No!' It was an anguished cry from the heart which Claire couldn't repress.

'Oh yes.' Marianne was slowly pushing her chair away from the table and now she rose to her feet, her slim body regal in its vivid scarlet. 'But even so he won't be willing to share you, my dear.' Her voice had softened as though she already knew she had scored her point. 'How foolish of you to encourage that young man to visit you during Jake's absence.'

'I didn't!' Claire cried. She didn't intend to let Marianne see the pain she was inflicting, but it was impossible to hide, when every word seemed to be cutting into her like a thousand knives.

Marianne was walking towards the door and she paused as she reached it, her pale blue eyes flickering over Claire's taut figure. 'Then I advise you to tell him so immediately,' she murmured with a cool little smile. 'But I must warn you that he's not in a very sympathetic mood this afternoon.'

Claire was stunned. She stared at Marianne, horror

in her eyes. Jake had returned and Marianne had already seen him. 'Jake's back?' she whispered hoarsely, already knowing the answer but unable to keep silent.

'Oh yes, he's back. He's in the office if you want to speak to him.'

The door closed behind her very gently and Claire stayed exactly where she was, staring at its smooth wooden panels, a dazed expression in her green eyes. Jake had returned when she was out and he knew everything, more than everything as he'd already heard Marianne's version of the story. What ought she to do? She was so confused, so unhappy. She couldn't get Marianne's taunting words out of her brain. She wouldn't allow herself to believe they were true and yet she still couldn't forget them.

Slowly she pushed herself to her feet. She would have to go and face Jake immediately. There was no other solution. She left the dining room and walked quietly down the corridor before her courage deserted her completely. The office door loomed in front of her all too quickly. She hesitated in front of it for a moment and then raised her hand and knocked sharply, a brisk tattoo which sounded loud and aggressive. There was no reply but somehow she knew that Jake was in there, he just wasn't intending to open the door. She took another shaky breath. She had nothing to lose. She couldn't leave without speaking to him now. It would take her hours to build up sufficient courage to try again.

She put her fingers over the door handle and pushed, half-expecting it to be locked, but it opened smoothly and she stepped inside, legs shaking, her chin raised as though preparing to resist a blow. The room was bright after the gloom of the passageway and it took a moment for her eyes to adjust, and then she saw that Jake was there, his dark head bent as he stared at a pile of papers on his desk. But Claire sensed that he wasn't really seeing them. He was as tormentingly aware of her presence as she was of him, only he wasn't going to look up.

Claire took one step forward and then another, wishing she could control the way her pulses raced whenever she was with him, wishing she could slow her wildly pounding heartbeats, wishing she didn't always feel quite so weak and clinging the moment he appeared. He raised his head at last and she stopped dead, the blast from his cold blue eyes slamming like a hammer blow on to her skull. She swayed on her feet as though he had indeed physically assaulted her.

'Jake, please,' she whispered. 'Don't look at me like that.' Her skin felt icy as his cold eyes flicked over her.

'How ought I to look at you, Claire?' His voice was harsh, grating on her ears. 'Ought I to stride forward and take you passionately into my arms?' he continued remorselessly, leaning on to the desk, his hands balled fists in front of him. 'Is that the way you prefer your lovers to greet you?'

'Jake, you've got to let me explain,' Claire pleaded. 'I didn't invite Alan, honestly I didn't. I was horrified when he arrived.'

He watched her, tormented loathing in the blue depths of his eyes. 'Marianne told me just how horrified you were.'

'Alan Crosby kissed me. I didn't return his embrace!' she cried. She began to walk towards him, green eyes pleading. 'Honestly Jake.'

The look in his eyes stopped her in her tracks.

'My God, Claire! I don't think you know the meaning of the word honesty. You've been cheating on me from the word go, only I was so damned green I couldn't see past that beautiful welcoming smile or that sexy little body. I wanted to believe you. Christ, I was a fool!' He pushed himself to his feet and moved jerkily over to the window, staring out, his back to Claire. 'I won't let you do this to me any longer,' he muttered at last. 'We're finished, Claire! It's over between us! You can go back to Alan Crosby or Mike Brent or whoever you damn well please. But leave me out of your plans from now on. God knows, I've had enough.'

There was pain as well as fury and contempt in his voice but Claire didn't hear it. She was too busy fighting her own weakness, struggling not to cry. His words had torn her to shreds and it showed. She bent her head to hide her face but still she knew he had turned and was watching her, waiting for her to speak, but the words stuck fast in her throat. If he cared at all, surely he ought to have been willing to give her a hearing before judging her, but he had made his decision, he wasn't going to listen. What was the point in trying to protest her innocence?

Her face was very pale, her green eyes enormous, glazed with tears which didn't fall. She raised her head, gathering the tattered remnants of her pride around her like a cloak. As Marianne had told her, Jake didn't care. She meant a moment's passing desire to him, that was all.

'I'm sorry it had to end like this,' she whispered.

Jake's colour faded and he took a step away from the window. 'You're admitting it then? You're saying it's true?' he muttered hoarsely.

Claire shook her head wearily. Her whole body felt defeated, as though her adrenalin had drained away down to the last drop. She knew that life would go on and she would go on with it but at this moment all she wanted to do was run away and hide. 'I'm admitting nothing, Jake,' she said, her voice very low. 'I told you the truth. I can't help it if you don't believe me.'

Before he could say anything else, before he even realised what she intended, she turned and moved towards the door. It seemed a long way to Claire, her head held high, walking slowly, when all she really wanted to do was run, but she managed it at last. She didn't look round once, but closed the door quietly behind her. Thank God it was Sunday she thought as she reached the quiet sanctuary of her room. She wouldn't have to put on an act. She wouldn't have to pretend to anyone.

The tears came then, pouring down her cheeks,

soaking her pillow, leaving her body limp and exhausted. Jake had hurt her badly today, but she was partly to blame. She had given far too much of herself, too soon. But if nothing else she had learned her lesson. It would be a long time before she allowed any man to approach half as close to her as Jake Svenson had done.

CHAPTER TEN

AT the end of June the weather turned around completely, leaden skies and steady, depressing drizzle lowering the horizon and turning the glorious blue sea into a threatening, white-capped grey. Claire was worried for a while that it would delay production. Somehow the thought of even an extra day, an extra hour, on set, watching Jake, speaking to him, having to pretend that everything was fine, was a special sort of agony for her. So that when filming continued to progress at the same hectic pace as usual she felt nothing but relief.

And now at last, her final day on set had arrived. Claire was freezing. She shivered in the cold, damp air blowing directly from the sea and pulled her dark cloak more securely around her shoulders, her eyes narrowing slightly against the wind as she peered into the bay below her. The men were already in position and the camera would pan down from herself and Marianne on the cliff top to show the fight taking place between the wreckers and the soldiers on the beach.

The wind gusted suddenly, flicking the damp folds of her skirt around her legs, her hair blowing in a bronze-red cloud invading her eyes and her mouth so that she put up a hand to wipe it away. She struggled for a moment longer with the wind and then gave up the unequal battle, turning with a sigh, her back to the elements. She could see that the crew were still struggling to anchor their equipment, the grassy cliff top a hive of frenzied activity with Jake Svenson in the very centre of it.

Claire watched him with pain in her eyes. He was tired and wet and looked as cold as she was herself, his dark hair slicked damply to his scalp, his green cagoule flapping open in the wind. Why must she be such a fool? she asked herself angrily. Even now, after all that had happened, she was still as much in love with him as ever. What was it about him that compelled her love? she wondered. What made her go right on loving him when she knew perfectly well that he didn't return her feelings? Love had grown so slowly, so stealthily, that it had taken her unawares. The first small seed of attraction had flourished and grown into a gigantic oak tree and Claire was afraid that its roots were too deeply embedded for her ever to break completely free of them again.

Jake was talking to Al Denton, the director of photography, but now, as Claire watched, Marianne walked up to him, wrapped like Claire in the dark woollen cloak required by the script. Claire's heart twisted painfully in her breast. She still couldn't watch the two of them together without feeling the same familiar ache. She still didn't know whether Jake was in love with Marianne, but she suspected it must be so. He was so very warm and kind to her, his smile gentle, as it had never been when he looked at Claire.

But he wasn't smiling now, she realised. Marianne was gazing up at him anxiously, her beautiful face pale, her fingers plucking nervously at the sleeve of his jacket. She appeared to be arguing with him. Jake shook his dark head and Claire could read the angry flash of his eyes from where she was standing. Marianne said something more and was answered with a sharp negative and then Claire froze, rooted to the spot, as Marianne's gaze swivelled unerringly in her direction, her blue eyes blazing at Claire, waves of pain and hatred seeming to reach out and clutch at her. The feeling was so strong that Claire retreated instinctively before it. Indeed, she thought for a moment that Marianne was going to walk forward and attack her physically. But then, without a word to anyone she whirled around and pushed her way angrily through the cameras and equipment littering the hillside.

Claire let out her pent-up breath in a small troubled

sigh. What did it mean? She felt sure that Jake and Marianne had been quarrelling and somehow she was concerned in it. But what had Jake said to make Marianne so angry? Claire turned her head on the thought. Jake was staring at her, his blue eyes burning into hers, and she couldn't look away.

She stood and shook like a leaf as Jake began to walk towards her, Al Denton following in his wake. He watched her every step of the way, blue, glittering eyes locked on to her face. He stopped in front of her, his hands shooting out, gripping her cold fingers between his own, Claire too stunned to try and pull them away.

'Claire, I've got to speak to you,' he began. He was talking quickly, his voice low and raw with emotion, but that was as much as he was able to say.

Al Denton appeared at his elbow, his worried brown eyes fixed on Jake, scarcely seeming to see Claire. 'Jake, what the hell am I going to do with that second camera? It's driving me nuts!'

Jake was still crushing Claire's fingers between his own, but now he turned his head, his jaw taut and said with a half-angry, half-impatient sigh, 'Can't it wait, Al? I need to speak to Claire urgently.'

'I'm sorry, Jake. We can't do a thing until it's settled.'

'Okay, I'll come,' Jake sighed again, surrendering Claire's hands reluctantly. He turned back to her, his eyes intent, trying to convey a message which she still didn't understand. 'I'll see you later, Claire, okay?' he murmured.

She nodded, biting her lip as he turned away with Al. He had barely spoken to her for weeks and now this. There had been passion in his eyes when he looked at her. What was she supposed to think? Was this some sort of sadistic game he was playing, with her as the victim? She was still in the same position, head bent, her eyes fixed on the damp grass, when Dave Tillson came to fetch her for the final scene. Still her eyes searched for Jake, but he was in a huddle with Al and the second camera and his bent head told her nothing.

Dave squeezed her arm and she forced her attention back towards him. He smiled, 'This is it, Claire. The last lap. Good luck, my love . . . from all of us.'

Claire smiled back, touched, her wide green eyes filled with tears. 'Thanks Dave,' she murmured. Everyone on the film had been so kind. If only things had worked out between Jake and herself it would have been a wonderful experience.

'Ready please.' That was Dave's voice calling out the warning and Claire dragged her thoughts back to the scene ahead. Marianne had already moved into position ready to walk towards her, blonde hair flying loose around her head, giving her a strange, almost demented appearance. The cameras started rolling and Marianne moved threateningly towards Claire as the script called for her to do. Claire tried to concentrate on her lines, but it was amazingly difficult. She was sure that Marianne had positioned herself deliberately, so that she had to stand frighteningly near to the edge of the precipice. Claire tried to banish from her memory the brief glimpse she had had of a dizzying drop, ending on needle sharp rocks, breathing steadily and deeply. 'Don't give up now, Claire. This is the last time,' she told herself bracingly.

Marianne glared at her, blue eyes fiercely glittering. 'They've killed John and you're to blame,' she hissed through clenched white teeth. 'You brought the soldiers here!'

Claire quivered, a hysterical desire to giggle piercing her fear. This was not acting. She could have played this scene without a script. She didn't need to pretend; she was terrified.

Claire stepped back a pace, trying to retreat, but Marianne's gloved hand shot out, preventing her escape. 'You think you've won . . . but you haven't, Désirée de Bourgogne,' she cried. She was breathing hard, as though she'd been running, her small white teeth bared in an almost animal snarl.

Claire winced, pulling away again as Marianne's

fingers dug into her arm, raising livid weals on her white flesh. Marianne laughed now and released one of Claire's arms, pointing over the cliff to the beach below. 'Your lover's down there. You think he's safe in the village, but he's not. The soldiers will kill him, too. You will never see him again.'

While she was speaking Marianne had taken another step nearer to the cliff edge, pulling Claire along with her. Claire heard Jake's shout of, 'Cut,' and then, 'For God's sake step back from the edge, Marianne!' But Marianne herself seemed not to hear him. She leaned out dizzyingly over the drop, the wind whipping her skirts, as though searching for her lover on the beach below. And as Claire watched Marianne's head jerked suddenly towards the ground at her feet. There was no sound but Claire could see that the earth was moving, crumbling silently away.

Marianne's grip on Claire's arm loosened as she sought to step backwards, but already it was too late. Claire was mute, helpless, rooted to the uncertain ground. It was all happening so quickly, it was unreal, a terrifying nightmare from which she would waken any minute. She saw Marianne's hand thrown out, fingers splayed in terror, begging for help, and there was a voice in her head, screaming Jake's name over and over again. Next minute she had clutched Marianne's fingers in her own and was falling with her, scrabbling hands trying to get a grip on the crumbling earth as she fell to her knees and slid to the edge of the precipice and then slowly but with frightening certainty, over the edge.

It was cold and Claire shivered uncontrollably as she listened to the voice which hammered with relentless persistence at her feeble brain. 'Claire, you must wake up! You can't be dead! Dear God, I didn't mean it! I only meant to frighten you.'

Claire knew it was Marianne's voice, but she didn't understand its significance, Marianne sounded horrified, beside herself with fear. Were they still filming? Claire wondered dazedly. Had she suffered a momentary blackout and missed her cue? She groaned aloud and tried to sit up but there seemed to be a heavy weight pinning her to the ground.

'Claire, are you all right? For God's sake, answer me.'

That was surely Jake's voice. It was true then, she must have fainted during filming. Claire tried to open her eyes, but her lids were too heavy, as though weighted down by lead.

'She's moved, Jake. Don't worry, she's alive!'

That was Marianne again and she sounded to be crying. It was all too difficult for Claire to understand. She was tired, very tired. It was easier to drift along, not bothering to move. She could have slept if Jake and Marianne hadn't kept shouting over her head.

'Can't you reach her, Marianne?' That was Jake's voice again, harsh with fear. 'Try to bring her round! If she moves too far she'll go over the edge!'

'Jake, Jake, she's moving again. Oh God!' Through the dazed, tortuous mists of her brain Claire dimly heard Marianne's terrified words. But there was pain now, her head throbbing as though tiny men with hammers were standing behind her beating on her skull. She began to move restlessly, her heavy limbs threshing wildly.

'The ledge is crumbling!' Marianne's voice rose to a crescendo beside Claire's ear, increasing the splitting pain in her head.

'For God's sake waken her, Marianne! We're sending for help but there's nothing else we can do until then.' Jake's voice seemed to come from a great distance, his tones hoarse and ragged, rough with emotion as he added, 'We haven't even got a blasted rope and the cliff's far too unstable for me to climb down. We would all go over the edge. You've just got to waken her! Try, Marianne! Try!'

'I can't, I can't move, I've tried already.' Marianne's voice shook, ragged with fear and pain and from a great distance Claire heard Jake's groan of desperation. Slowly she forced her trembling lids to open just a fraction. For a moment the sky swung dizzily, grey clouds above stunted trees growing on a sheer cliffside.

Very slowly she raised a hand and pressed it to her aching lids. 'What's happened? Where am I?' The hoarse, whispered words echoed the fear and confusion in her brain.

'She's coming round! It's all right, Jake!' Marianne's high-pitched tones jarred in Claire's throbbing head.

She groaned, the whispered words forced past her dry lips. 'Please Marianne, don't shout like that.'

Marianne's shaky reply came from behind Claire's head. 'I'm sorry, Claire. I'm sorry.' She sounded to be half-laughing, half-crying. 'You'll understand in a moment, but whatever you do, don't move. Not an inch! We're trapped on a ledge about half way down the cliff. At the moment it's holding, but it's not very solid. Keep still . . . just keep very still!'

Claire wanted to move, she wanted to thrust herself to her feet and run. But she was trapped in a nightmare of pain and incomprehension. She could see nothing but the drifting clouds and the gaunt cliff. Involuntarily she groaned again, clenching her teeth on the sound.

'Don't worry, Claire. We fell down the cliff and I think you must have banged your head on the way down. That's why you feel so odd.' Marianne again, speaking quickly, her tones taut with the self-control she was exerting. 'If you keep still everything will be fine. They've already gone for help. You've been unconscious for ages.'

Jake's voice came again now from somewhere far above them. 'Claire darling, can you hear me?'

Claire had a sudden desperate urge to see his face and she moved unthinkingly, pushing with her hands against the earth, trying to lever her body erect. It was the last thing she remembered. She screamed aloud, waves of pain shooting from wrist to shoulder. Jake was shouting her name, but she fell back limply on to the ground, her lids closing as she lost consciousness completely.

She woke to a dusky evening light, illuminating a white-painted room; and almost unbearable pain. Her right arm throbbed viciously and her vision whirled and twisted in a hazy, pulsating mist of anguish. She was still in a nightmare and it seemed impossible to escape. She tried to lift her head, desperate to see her surroundings but she moaned aloud and collapsed back on to her pillow as pain took over once again, clouding her vision, filming her brow with a sheen of sweat.

Immediately the seated figure at the side of her bed moved, peering into her face. 'Where am I?' Claire whispered. Those little men with hammers were at it again, pounding relentlessly at her skull.

'You're in hospital, Miss Grant. Don't you remember?' It was a young voice, gentle and reassuring. Claire's heavy lids lifted, her green eyes focusing slowly on the uniformed figure. And then with a groan she closed them again. She remembered now. She remembered everything in vivid technicolour detail.

'It was horrible.' She moved her head weakly on the pillow, bright strands of bronze-gold feathering the white linen. 'I thought I was dead.'

The nurse leaned forward and adjusted her pillows gently. 'You were both very lucky,' she murmured.

Claire's eyes flew open. Of course, she hadn't been alone. 'Marianne, is she all right?' she whispered. They had both fallen down the cliff face and neither of them had been able to move, she remembered. Fear rose in her throat like sickness. 'What's wrong with me? Why am I here?' Her voice sounded sharp, panicky, and she tried to sit up again so that the nurse had to push her back, tucking her gently but firmly beneath the sheets.

'You've got a deep gash on your skull,' she replied patiently. 'You mustn't touch it and dislodge the dressing. Your ribs are cracked and your right arm is damaged. But you'll do.' Her hands were busy smoothing the crisp, white sheets as she talked. 'As for Miss Lejeune, I'm afraid she has damaged her spine. But you mustn't worry, the doctors feel confident that her injuries aren't as bad as we thought at first.'

Claire sighed heavily. She could hear the nurse moving around the room, but she closed her eyes, trying to block out harsh reality. With the return of her memory so much had come rushing back. So much that she didn't want to remember.

'Miss Lejeune has already had one operation,' the nurse was saying now in calming tones. 'She should be coming round from her anaesthetic soon. Mr Svenson's with her at the moment.' She smiled. 'I know he'll be coming in to see you before he leaves the building. He will be able to tell you more himself.'

'Thank you.' Claire felt unutterably weary and she closed her eyes tightly on the hot tears which burned behind her lids. Jake and Marianne were together. It was what she ought to have expected of course, but still it hurt. It was crazy of her to remember that brief moment on the cliff top when Jake had tried to speak to her. It had meant nothing. It was Marianne that he loved.

The white-capped figure at her side leaned forward anxiously. 'Are you in a great deal of pain, Miss Grant?'

Claire nodded. 'Yes,' she murmured weakly. 'A very great deal.' The pain of imagining Jake and Marianne together was still too much to bear. Her physical ills were milk and water things in comparison. An arm around her shoulders supported Claire momentarily and she swallowed the tablets which were popped into her mouth without question.

The nurse lowered her to the pillow. 'Try to sleep now,' she insisted quietly. 'You'll feel much better tomorrow.'

The words held no promise for Claire. She knew the pain of her love for Jake would be with her for a long time to come. But whatever was in the tablets they

achieved at least a part of their objective, dulling the
pain in her arm and head until she eventually achieved
some kind of oblivion. But it was a fitful sleep and she
woke on one occasion to almost complete consciousness.
It was night, a softly shaded lamp burning at one side
of the bed. There were two people in her room and she
turned her head slightly, but they were shadowy figures
beyond the edge of her vision.

'Pulse and temperature are not too bad.'

'That's reassuring,' the second voice replied.

'She's in considerable discomfort but she definitely
regained full consciousness.'

'Has he been told?' the second voice asked.

'Oh yes.' The soft feminine voice sounded positive.
'I've had difficulty in persuading him that she won't
surface again for some time. I told him I'd given her the
medication the doctor prescribed and he ought to get
some sleep himself while he could.' A laugh. 'He's
rather gorgeous, isn't he? I might be tempted to fall
down a cliff myself if I thought it would bring him to
the rescue.'

The voices were retreating and Claire struggled to
hear the reply. Somehow she knew the words held some
significance for her but she was too tired to struggle
with the problem any longer. Her eyes closed.

It was full daylight before she woke again. And she
was falling, a fierce rushing of wind and the sound of
storm-tossed waves in her ears. The rocks were jagged
needles waiting just for her and this time there was
nothing to save her. She jerked upright in bed, her
uninjured hand pressed hard to her mouth to stem a cry
of pure terror.

'No! Oh no! Don't let it happen, please!' Her eyes flew
to the figure at her side, huge and green and fear
stricken. She expected it to be the young nurse but
instead it was Jake's tormented gaze which met her
own.

He was sitting on the bed at her side and his hands
shot out and gripped her shoulders. 'Claire you're safe

now. I promise you I shan't let it happen again. It was a
dream . . . only a dream.' His tones were raw, anguished
as he stared at her terrified expression.

For a brief moment Claire forgot everything but her
burning, hungry need to be with him. 'Jake, oh Jake!
Help me!' she cried and with a choked sob threw herself
into his arms and clung to him helplessly, her face
buried in his broad chest.

He held her tightly, his mouth pressed against her
sweat-dampened hair. 'Claire . . . Claire, I've been so
worried.' His voice was husky, muffled as his mouth
moved in her hair. 'When I saw you both disappearing
over the cliff I thought I was going to die.'

His hoarse words brought Claire back to reality with
a jolt. She had forgotten Marianne, forgotten everything
but her need of him, but now it all came rushing back.
She had no right to be here in Jake's arms. He was
holding her like this because he felt sorry for her, that
was all. It was Marianne that he loved.

But still she didn't move immediately. Surely she was
entitled to something? Surely even Marianne wouldn't
begrudge her this one brief moment. She clung to him
for a few more precious seconds, revelling in the
warmth and strength of him, feeling the rough denim of
his shirt beneath her skin, hearing the rapid beating of
his heart. She loved him. She loved him so much. But it
was no use. With a tremendous effort she pulled herself
away, holding her head erect, only her trembling lips
betraying her vulnerable emotions.

'I'm sorry,' she whispered. 'I was so frightened.'

He gazed at her, his blue eyes warm and disturbingly
tender and Claire trembled in his grip. 'Don't be sorry.
You've been wonderful, Claire. You risked your life for
Marianne. Believe me, you don't need to apologise for
anything. I'm the one who ought to apologise. I ought
never to have let either of you stand where you did, but
I just didn't notice until it was to late.' He shook his
head, dark strands of hair falling on to his forehead. 'I
don't think I shall ever forgive myself.'

'It wasn't your fault, Jake. You mustn't blame yourself.' Claire flopped wearily back on to the pillows and fought desperately with the urge to cry. He was sorry for her and she couldn't stand that, not just now.

'Claire, I shall always blame myself.' He reached out a hand as though to take her own in his grasp. But Claire avoided it, raising her hand to her head, probing the bandage on her skull with trembling fingers. She knew if he touched her once again in her present weakened state she would break down completely and all the weak, pleading words that she knew she hadn't to say, would come rushing out.

'How is Marianne?' she asked now, her voice shaking. He was looking at her so strangely that she couldn't meet his eyes, but stared instead at the white, cotton counterpane beneath her fingers.

'We don't know yet, not for sure.' His tones had thickened, heavy with pain and Claire wanted to cry again but was determined not to, blinking back tears with fierce concentration.

'I'm sorry, I'm very sorry,' she whispered. 'I know how worried you must be.'

'I have been worried,' Jake agreed huskily. 'In fact I've been going half out of my mind, thinking of you both lying injured and helpless on that ledge.' His eyes dropped to her injured arm and before Claire could guess his intention he lowered his head swiftly and placed a brief, hungry kiss on her fingers where they emerged from the clumsy plaster. His own hand closing tightly over the cold flesh, warm and strong.

Claire flinched away as though he had stabbed her.

'Do you hate me touching you so much?' His voice was as low and impassioned as that brief touch of his lips had been. 'You must do ... of course you must, after the way I've treated you. But I can't help it, I need to touch you. I thought you were dead. I thought I'd lost you.' He raised his head and Claire gave a small gasp and closed her eyes tightly.

'Please Jake, don't do this!' she cried. 'Don't say these things. Not when you know you don't mean them.' She began to sob helplessly, tears pouring from under her eyelids and down her cheeks.

With a muttered exclamation Jake's arms closed around her, his mouth covering her face with featherlight kisses. 'Don't cry, darling, please. I can't bear to see you like this. I've been such a fool.' He raised one arm, stroking her cheek with unsteady fingers. 'Can't you bear to look at me, Claire? Do you hate me so much?' He paused, staring at her, his hard mouth not quite steady. 'I can't blame you for feeling like this. I behaved like a brute. But you hurt me, Claire. You made me feel weak and vulnerable and I hated it. I had to hit back. Even though it meant that I hurt myself as well.'

Claire raised her trembling lids. 'Oh Jake, don't say any more. I can't take it, not today.' She saw his face and moved her head slowly from side to side on the supporting pillows. 'I don't hate you,' she whispered. 'And you mustn't blame yourself for what happened. It was an accident. You don't need to make amends. I understand how you feel, believe me I do. There's no need to say any more.' She did understand. He was grateful to her for saving Marianne and he pitied her. The knowledge was tearing her apart.

Jake leaned forward, his blue eyes blazingly intent, his voice low and unsteady. 'Claire, I want to explain. I want you to understand why I behaved as I did. Even if you still can't forgive me, I've got to tell you my reasons.'

Claire shook her head. 'Not now, Jake,' she whispered brokenly, the salt tears still trickling unchecked down her cheeks. 'I'm in pain, my head aches. I understand, believe me, I do. You don't need to explain or apologise and there's nothing to forgive. Just leave me now. I'd like to be alone.'

He pushed himself slowly to his feet, his face very pale, his tormented eyes fastened on her face. 'You're sending me away?'

Claire kept her eyes tightly closed. She couldn't look at him, knowing that if she did she would beg him to stay whatever his motives. She needed him, and at this moment even his pity was tempting. 'Yes, I'm sending you away. I'm tired, deathly tired. I need to be alone,' she murmured.

'I guess I can't blame you, Claire.' His tone was hoarse, his words tightly clipped as though he was exerting tremendous control. 'If you change your mind you only have to ask, and I'll come.' Then with one last agonised look at her trembling figure he turned on his heel and left the room.

The moment he closed the door Claire's tears came flooding out. She cried as though her heart would break, as indeed she thought it would. Jake had seemed to be offering her so much when in reality all his words had been motivated by pity and a misplaced sense of guilt. Claire's tears increased as she remembered the things he had said to her. If only she could have taken his words at face value, how happy she would have been.

The door into her room opened suddenly and Claire's brimming eyes flew towards it, half-hoping, half-fearing that Jake had returned. But it was the young nurse who entered. She took one look at Claire's distraught features and fled back along the corridor to fetch the sister. It was a relief for Claire when the sister in her turn fetched the white-coated doctor to her bedside and more pills and painkillers were prescribed, so that she was able once more to sink into a dazed state between sleeping and waking where serious thought became impossible.

Unfortunately even then Jake Svenson's shadowy figure continued to haunt her. Awake or sleeping she couldn't escape him. She knew she had to recover her health as quickly as possible. Only by putting actual physical distance between them could she hope to be free of his tormenting presence. With this aim in view she became a model patient. She never allowed anyone to see her crying again. If she drenched her pillow with tears it was in the secret watches of the night when the nurses on duty were safely at the other end of the corridor and there was no one to witness her pain.

Jake didn't come to visit her again. That hurt . . . badly. Of course, if he had come she would have had to send him away. She had spent many hours rehearsing the words she would use—their brief affair had been a mistake, she had realised that long before the accident, or so she intended to tell him. But the agonised rehearsals had been unnecessary. He had never appeared. She guessed he must be spending his time with Marianne.

Claire knew that the star was improving slowly because she had received a brief, dictated letter from her via the nurse. Not that she mentioned Jake in it. It read:

> 'Dear Claire, Please forgive me for involving you in the accident. I confess that I knew you were afraid of heights and deliberately tried to frighten you by forcing you to stand near the edge of the cliff—I think that by this time you will understand why! I certainly never intended to hurt you as I did. I know that you tried to save me, and this after I had behaved so very badly! What can I say? Except that I am sorry and hope in the future to have the opportunity to make amends.'

Claire cried a little over the note. It brought back too many memories. But she bore Marianne no grudge, not for anything. She had begun to realise the lengths to which jealousy could drive one. On her bad days, when she felt weak and helpless, she was still tempted to write to Jake, asking him to call and see her. Sometimes she just longed for a brief glimpse of his lean features and she knew at these times that she would have been content with anything he had to give.

By the end of the second week Claire was well enough to spend most of her day out of bed and she knew that she would be free to leave the hospital within the next few days. She'd received a number of frantic phone calls from her mother and had great difficulty in dissuading her from flying over immediately. She didn't want to be fussed. It would weaken her and she needed all the strength she could muster to fight the temptation to contact Jake. Instead she promised her mother that she would go to the States herself as soon as she was fit enough to travel the distance.

To her surprise, her agent had been among her very first visitors, bringing Lynn from London in the comfort of his Rolls. Lynn had been horrified when she walked into the hospital room and saw Claire, lying so weak and pale, bandages swathing her forehead and arm.

'Darling, what have they done to you?' she cried. 'I simply can't afford to let you out of my sight for a moment.' She was torn between laughter and tears and Claire felt the same. It was so good to see her. It would have been such a relief to break down and pour her troubles into Lynn's sympathetic ear, but her agent had entered the room just behind her friend, bluff and smiling, a large bunch of roses in his hand, and so instead of tears, Claire had forced a laugh.

'I may look like an Egyptian mummy but I'm not quite ready for the tomb just yet, so don't worry.'

Lynn had been forced to return to London that night as she had a modelling assignment the next morning but Claire had had an almost continuous stream of visitors since then. Practically everyone in the cast and crew of *Wrecker's Bride* having been to see her.

She sat in the chair now at the side of her bed, her gaze flickering round the tiny hospital room. Every available surface was covered with flowers. Some had even been given to other wards, she'd had so many delivered. But the small vase on her bedside table she'd insisted on keeping. Her eyes went to it now as she remembered the card which had accompanied the posy of pure white roses. There had been no flowery phrases, just a simple, 'To Claire. With all my love. From Jake.' But Claire knew that she would treasure that small card for the rest of her life.

The huge bowl of roses behind it was from Mike and Joan. Claire's eyes softened. Dear Mike, he had been so upset to see her like this.

'I was on the beach when you fell,' he told her on his first visit. 'My God, Claire, I couldn't believe it was happening. I was up those steps and on to the cliff top at twice the speed of light.'

'I couldn't believe it was happening myself,' Claire confessed with a shaky laugh. 'It still doesn't seem real.'

'You were so lucky,' Mike murmured. 'But whatever possessed you to hang on to Marianne as you did? You must have known you couldn't save her.'

Claire raised her shoulders. She had wondered the same thing herself, often. Reliving those horrifying moments when she began to slide over the cliff. 'Instinct, I guess,' she said now. 'I'm still not really sure myself. It just seemed the right thing to do at the time,' she murmured, her eyes on the small square of window and the blue skies beyond it. 'I'm certainly no heroine, far from it. I don't think I would do it again.' She shivered suddenly, remembering the way the rocks and the sea had seemed to be rushing up to meet her. 'In fact, I'm sure I wouldn't.'

'Svenson was practically crying with relief when they brought you up on the stretcher.' Mike was staring at her, his dark eyes intent. 'I was pretty near to tears myself, if the truth be known.'

Claire bent her head, plucking helplessly at the covers. 'Jake's been very kind.' Mike's words were tearing her apart. It was agony having to lie in bed and listen, worse agony having to answer him and he still hadn't finished.

'Has he, Claire? Has he really?' Mike muttered. 'Then how come things are still not right between you? Why is he walking around looking more like a ghost with every day that passes?'

Claire raised her head, her eyes hot with the pressure of unshed tears. 'He's worried about Marianne. You must know that,' she whispered.

'Marianne's improving steadily. The doctors say she'll definitely walk again.' Mike's words rolled on relentlessly.

Claire moved her head. 'He blames himself for the accident. I told him he needn't.'

'That's not why he's eating his heart out,' Mike exclaimed. 'Why have you stopped seeing him?' he demanded. 'What maggot have you got into that idiotic skull of yours at this stage? I can't believe you really don't want to see him.'

'I don't,' Claire choked, turning bruised eyes to Mike's sympathetic face. 'He pities me, Mike. He knows how I feel about him and he pities me. I can't bear it!'

'If it's pity that's turning him into a walking skeleton, I for one shall be very surprised. I take it he's been to see you and done some much-needed apologising and you've sent him on his way?'

'Oh Mike, it wasn't like that!' She could see from his face that Mike didn't understand. She wasn't even sure that she understood herself.

'Oh no?' Mike's tone was frankly sceptical. 'Claire Grant, sometimes I wonder just what goes on in that head of yours.' He flicked the soft curve of her cheek with a gentle finger. 'Maybe the shock of the fall has addled your brain. Jake Svenson's in love with you, not Marianne, and you're ruining your best chance of getting together again for the sake of your stupid pride.' He saw her expression but continued ruthlessly. 'Because that's all it is, Claire, I thought he was a blind idiot but now I'm beginning to think that you're both well suited.'

Claire was forced into weak laughter, her soft mouth curving into the first spontaneous smile she'd given for days.

'That's better.' Mike smiled too, squeezing her fingers gently. 'Think about what I've said ... and do something about it. Before it's too late!'

CHAPTER ELEVEN

CLAIRE walked along the corridor, carefully examining the numbers on the closed doors. It was her last day in the hospital. Tomorrow she was going back to London and then to the States to stay with her mother and stepfather. But before she could escape completely she had one more ordeal to suffer. Marianne, although recovering slowly, was still bedridden and she had begged Claire to visit her before she left. Claire's first instinct had been to refuse. But she knew it would be cowardly to do so. Jake loved Marianne and she had to face it, and avoiding the other woman wouldn't help her to do that.

But she sighed now, pausing outside one of the closed doors, examining the paper in her hand. Marianne's room number was thirty-nine and this was thirty-seven. She moved slowly onwards, stopping when she reached Marianne's room. The door was firmly closed, not a sound from within, but without giving herself time for second thoughts she tapped lightly and turned the handle.

The colour and perfume of the ranks of flowers was the first thing she noticed. It was a small room like her own and the scent of exotic blooms was almost overpowering. Her eyes went instinctively, foolishly, to the bedside table. There were no white roses, but of course Jake would have sent flowers to the woman he loved. Probably the dozens of huge red blooms filling one entire window sill.

At last her eyes turned towards the bed. She'd deliberately delayed the moment, she realised. She was afraid of Marianne, jealousy still a naked, open wound. Her gaze travelled slowly up the white counterpane. Marianne was lying flat, her body very still, protected from the bedclothes by a long metal cage. Her eyes were closed, deep hollows in her grey face, her blonde hair, dull and lifeless, spread over the sheets.

Claire stared, stricken, her green eyes shadowed with compassion. She didn't want to feel pity for Marianne, they had hated each other for too long, but she couldn't help it. She took an instinctive step forward, her feet scraping on the tiled floor and at last Marianne's eyes opened, very blue, huge lustrous pools drowning her pale face.

'Claire.' One hand stirred and Claire's legs moved forward of their own volition. 'Sit down if you would.' Marianne's voice was a weak echo of its usual rich, warm tones and Claire hurried to obey.

She knew she ought to speak, but she was mute, her mouth dry, stunned by Marianne's wasted beauty, and it was Marianne who broke the silence once again.

'How are you, Claire?' It was clearly an effort even for her to whisper, her lips barely moving. 'Nurse tells me you're being allowed home today.'

'Yes.' Claire found her voice at last. 'My arm's still a nuisance but otherwise I'm fine.' She paused, trying to smile. 'But how are you feeling? They tell me you're improving steadily.' Claire couldn't force any conviction into her words. Marianne looked dreadful. She looked as though she was dying. No wonder Jake was tearing himself apart.

But Marianne smiled faintly. 'I'm better, much better.' But even as she spoke she closed her eyes for a moment, breathing deeply, as though the effort had been too much for her.

Claire was instantly concerned. 'I've tired you, I'm sorry. Shall I fetch the nurse? Can I get you anything?'

'No, stay.' Marianne reached out and held her wrist with surprising strength. 'I must talk to you Claire.' She broke off, her tones unsteady. 'I meant what I said in the letter,' she whispered. 'I tried to frighten you deliberately. I knew you were afraid of heights.' The stark words came out in a rush and Claire squeezed the fingers that had been holding hers reassuringly.

'It doesn't matter, honestly. I understand.'

'I was jealous,' Marianne continued faintly. 'Wildly, uncontrollably jealous. I still am.' Her lips twisted into a painful smile. 'But no doubt it will pass.'

Claire shook her head, feeling herself flush painfully. This was far worse than she'd expected. Marianne's words sliced into her like knives, but they had to be answered. 'You don't need to be jealous,' she insisted quietly. 'If Jake ever felt anything for me it was over long ago.' Claire forced herself to say the words and she forced herself to listen and understand them, even though it hurt like hell. 'It's you he loves, Marianne. He's only been to see me once since the accident . . .'

'Really, darling,' the laughter sounded shocking coming from that pale, wasted figure on the bed, 'you don't honestly believe that, do you?' She saw Claire's face and sighed, a weak, thready sound. 'My goodness you're as big a fool as Jake himself.'

Claire stared at Marianne in amazement, her cheeks flushed as she tried to assimilate her words. What did Marianne mean? Had Jake not told her that he loved her? She was still wrestling with her fruitless speculations when the door behind her opened. Jake was on the threshold, his blue eyes shocked as they gazed into hers. And Claire stared back at him. Jake was ill! His eyes dark-shadowed, the strong bones of his face jutting in stark outline. Claire wanted to run and take him in her arms. It was agony having to sit quietly, next to Marianne, knowing that she had no right to touch him, knowing that it was anxiety for Marianne that was making him look like this.

He was still in the doorway watching them both silently, a flush darkening his cheekbones, his eyes moving slowly from one to the other of them.

'Come in, darling,' Marianne murmured. 'And close the door behind you.'

He still hesitated in the doorway, but then as though he had suddenly made up his mind, he moved. 'I'll come back later. You and Claire will want to talk.'

He can't bear to be near me, Claire thought in anguish. It was torture for her to see him again like this, but it would be even worse if he left.

'Running away again, Jake?' Marianne's voice cut through Claire's thoughts with surprising strength.

Jake stopped, his flush deepening, turning a hunted glance in Claire's direction. 'For God's sake, Marianne,' he protested. 'What are you trying to do?'

'I'm trying to knock some sense into your thick skull,' Marianne muttered remorselessly.

Claire sat very still, very pale, her head bent, her hands clenched tightly in her lap, listening, but totally confused. What was Marianne saying and why was Jake looking at her like that? It didn't make any kind of sense to Claire.

Marianne had closed her eyes as though suddenly very weary, but now she flicked them open again, looking at Jake. 'You're a fool, my darling. You're both fools.' She paused, breathing deeply, her fingers clutching the white counterpane. 'And maybe I'm an even bigger fool, trying to help you. But I owe Claire something. She tried to save my life and risked her own in the process. It was a brave thing to do and I doubt whether I would have done as much.' Her voice had slowed to a whisper, but now it stopped completely and there was silence in the room. Claire kept her head down but still she knew that Jake was watching her, tension gnawing inside her until every muscle in her body seemed to have frozen tight.

At last Marianne spoke again, turning to Jake, 'I owe you something too, darling,' she whispered. 'If my career's a success it's thanks to you. Unfortunately, that wasn't enough for me. I wanted everything. Poor Jake, these last weeks of filming have been hell for you, haven't they?' There was regret in her voice as she murmured. 'I'm sorry. I've been a bitch. I saw that you were attracted to Claire from the first day she arrived.'

Claire made a small strangled sound in her throat, but Marianne carried on as though oblivious. 'I tried to

create trouble between you from the very beginning.
The boy who kissed Claire, I knew she didn't like it, I
saw she was trying to fight him off. But I was so crazy
with jealousy that I was willing to use any weapon to
part you. And I knew that would.'

She was staring across the room at Jake's still figure.
'You understand, don't you darling?' she whispered at
last. 'You've been there too, haven't you? I saw the way
you watched Claire. I saw what jealousy was doing to
you. It tore you apart if she so much as looked at
another man.'

This was too much, Claire was trembling so violently
that she couldn't control it any longer. Marianne was
talking about her as though she was a statue and
nothing that she said made any sense. Claire pushed
herself to her feet, refusing to listen any longer. 'Please,
don't talk about this, Marianne. It's all in the past,' she
jerked out.

Marianne was breathing roughly, very tired. 'Nonsense, my dear.' She reached out and gripped Claire's
hand, a slender ivory manacle preventing Claire's
escape. 'I think you're in love with Jake.'

'Please,' Claire cried, pulling away, 'let me go.' What
was Marianne trying to do to her? Hadn't she suffered
enough?

'And Jake's in love with you.'

'Please, Marianne.' Claire's colour had gone from red
to chalk white in the space of a few seconds.

'He would have told you so himself before filming
finished, only I begged him not to do so,' Marianne
persisted with the tenacity of someone who knows her
strength is almost gone. 'I was distraught. I threatened
to ruin the last take.'

Suddenly Jake was very near. Claire could feel his
hard body almost touching hers, his breath on her
cheek. Claire's own breathing had stopped, pulses
hammering wildly at her wrist and throat. Could she
have made a mistake? Could Marianne be telling the
truth?

'Claire.' Just her name on Jake's lips gave her an electric shock, his tones low and husky with emotion.

Claire tried to fight it, still not ready to believe what her instincts were telling her. 'Please I . . .'

'Claire,' he said again, his fingers on her shoulders, digging in to the soft wool of her sweater. 'Claire, we've got to talk,' he murmured hoarsely.

Claire could feel his heart hammering wildly next to her backbone. Could it be true? she wondered. Could he possibly love her as Marianne said? She wanted to believe it quite desperately.

Jake's arms stole around her. 'Will you listen?' he whispered. 'Let me tell you how I feel.'

Claire's tongue was frozen to the roof of her mouth. 'Please Jake, I . . .' She never seemed to get any further than that faint protest.

'Listen, at least listen.' Jake's breathing was harsh and ragged, his body taut against her own. 'It's true, Claire. I do love you. I don't think I've slept since you sent me away. I'm going out of my mind. Won't you give me something to hope for? Tell me at least that you don't hate me.'

Claire was hardly aware that she'd turned in his arms, her green eyes huge and questioning, searching his face, looking for the truth. Seeing it in his eyes, hearing it in his slightly unsteady voice but still not quite able to believe that it was true. 'Are you telling me the truth, Jake?' she whispered.

He gripped her face tightly between his two palms. 'I love you, Claire. More than I would ever have dreamed possible.'

'Oh Jake!' Somehow she was in his arms, her face pressed against his chest. Perhaps she ought to have made him wait for his answer. She'd surrendered to him too quickly before, perhaps she was a fool, making the same mistake again. Only this time he'd surrendered too. He had told her that he loved her. She had waited a long time to hear him say just that, and now she wanted to believe it.

'I love you too, Jake,' she whispered into his shirt.

He took a fierce breath, his heartbeats accelerating crazily beneath her ear. And then his hand was beneath her chin, forcing it up so that he could see her face. 'You love me?' His voice was husky and his eyes searched her face, very intent. And then with a groan he had bent his head and was kissing her hungrily and she was kissing him back, her arms around his neck, holding him tight, forgetting everything but her deep, intense need for him.

He raised his head at last, gazing at her dazedly through his dark lashes.

'I'm very happy for you both. Now if you could find somewhere else to carry on this touching conversation, I could go to sleep, as I've been longing to do for the last half hour.' They had both forgotten Marianne, but now they turned their heads like sleepwalkers woken out of a particularly pleasant dream. She was smiling faintly, but she looked unutterably weary, her pale skin stretched tight over her delicate bones.

Jake's arm tightened around Claire's shoulders. 'Darling Marianne, I'm sorry. You must be exhausted.' He smiled into her eyes. 'But thank you.'

'Leave me now,' Marianne closed her eyes. 'Come back later . . . if Claire will let you.'

Jake and Claire walked for a long time in the hospital grounds after they'd left Marianne. The sky was blue, but with a cool wind rustling the branches of the trees and Jake kept his arm around Claire's shoulders, holding her close, his dark head bent as he talked, trying to explain why he had been so ready to mistrust her.

'Apart from the patently obvious reason that I was wildly jealous of any man who came within a mile of you,' he murmured with a faintly self-derisive laugh.

'You had no need to be jealous.' It seemed odd, saying that to Jake. She'd been so torn apart by jealousy herself that she felt he ought to be reassuring her. Except that it was no longer necessary. Thanks to

Marianne she had been given all the reassurance she needed.

'I know that now,' Jake said. 'I think I knew it then.' His voice deepened, harsh with remembered pain. 'But I was taught not to trust in a hard school. I'll spare you the boring details, but quite simply my mother was a tramp. She liked men and she didn't let marriage to my father affect the way she behaved. She was unfaithful constantly. He accepted that, but when she left him for someone else, that he couldn't take. He turned to alcohol for comfort and died when I was eleven. For obvious reasons I've found it very hard to trust any woman since then.'

The words sounded so much worse somehow, stated so calmly in that cold, clipped tone and Claire's eyes were full of pity for that lonely, disillusioned man and the small boy who had grown up too quickly. She could tell that it had hurt Jake to remember, but so many things that she hadn't understood were clear to her at last. No wonder he had reacted so strongly to her behaviour at the audition. She must have reminded him forcibly of his mother that day.

'Do you forgive me, Claire?' he muttered huskily now.

'Of course I do. I know I behaved badly at our first meeting. In fact I'm amazed that you were still attracted to me after that.'

Jake's smile was rueful. 'Shall I confess that I prayed very hard and very quietly that Dave would push for you to be given a part in the film. It was one hell of a relief when you gave such a tremendous audition. I knew the way I felt was crazy but I wanted you, badly, even then.'

They had stopped underneath an ancient oak tree and Claire leaned against the trunk, Jake's hands on either side of her face, the spreading green canopy of leaves and branches waving above them. He kissed her again and the branches of the old tree sighed in the wind as she clung to him breathlessly, returning his passionate kiss with a hunger as great as his own.

'I love you, I love you,' he groaned, the aching need
in his voice making her heart turn over. Marry me,
Claire . . . love me. I want to be with you.'

'Yes!' Claire laughed aloud, shouting the word, and a
blackbird which had been feeding in the undergrowth
flew away, chinking noisily.

Jake was laughing too, his blue eyes very warm. 'If
you're so determined to tell the world about it I think
this marriage had better be soon. How does tomorrow
sound to you?'

'Impossible . . . but marvellous,' Claire smiled, her
eyes alight with love for him. 'Oh Jake, I can hardly
believe this is happening.'

'I feel exactly the same,' Jake murmured into her
hair. 'When you sent me away after the accident I
didn't know what had hit me. It knocked me for six.
Why did you do it, Claire? Were you very angry with
me, darling?'

She shook her head. 'I wasn't angry. I just didn't
believe that you loved me,' she explained quietly. 'I
thought you felt sorry for me and guilty about the
accident. And I thought you loved Marianne.'

Jake's arms tightened around her. 'Crazy little idiot!
Surely you could see how I felt about you?'

'I don't think that I was seeing anything very clearly
just then,' she confessed. 'Mike said the fall had addled
my brain and I'm beginning to think that must have
been true.' She shivered slightly. 'It scares me to think
that if it hadn't been for Marianne I would have left
hospital today and possibly never seen you again.'

'I would have followed you, Claire,' Jake told her,
the look in his eyes bringing a surge of pink to her
cheeks. 'I was going to give you a few weeks to settle
down and then I was planning to come and see you
again. You wouldn't have escaped from me so easily,
my love.'

'But we owe Marianne a lot,' Claire insisted quietly.
She had a sudden picture of the star's frail figure lying
immobile in the hospital bed. Poor Marianne, she had

loved Jake and now she had lost him. Claire's green eyes were clouded. 'Oh Jake, I feel so sorry for her.'

'Don't worry, darling, she'll come round.' Jake sounded completely convinced. 'She thinks she loves me now but it's habit that's all. In reality she's married to the idea of being an actress, a star. She needs a good-natured, docile husband who will stay in the background.' His eyes darkened as he looked at Claire. 'And I can never be that. Once you're mine, Claire Grant, I never intend to let you go.'

Claire smiled contentedly into his eyes. She wouldn't have it any other way.

Claire stretched luxuriously in front of the full-length mirror, examining her elegant outline from every direction, and then she turned, her black evening dress swinging, moulding her hips as she moved. 'It was wonderful, Jake,' she sighed ecstatically. 'A marvellous evening. And you were right about Marianne. She was really in her element this evening. She loved every minute of the adulation and applause.' Marianne had had a handsome young actor by her side and to Claire's relief had treated Jake as nothing more than an old friend. '*Wrecker's Bride* is going to be a tremendous success,' she told him now.

Jake was smiling, his face relaxed in the mellow light from the standard lamp. 'Of course,' he agreed, his tones holding the faintest trace of self-mockery. 'What else did you expect?'

Claire laughed, pulling a small face. 'You can joke as much as you like about it, but the film was brilliantly directed. And it deserves to be a success.'

'I'm glad you recognise my many talents,' Jake murmured, teasing her again. Claire was an eye-catching figure this evening and he couldn't take his eyes off her. Slowly he loosened his tie, throwing it carelessly on to the bed. His dinner jacket followed and Claire returned his interest in full measure, watching as he slowly unfastened the buttons of his shirt and shrugged it off his broad shoulders, his body firm and tanned beneath it, the muscles of his chest rippling as his shirt followed his jacket on to the bed.

He beckoned slowly with one hand. 'Come over here.'

Claire touched her tongue provocatively to her lips. 'I don't know whether I will or not.'

'Then I shall have to come to you!' Jake moved towards her, his bare feet soundless on the thick pile of the carpet, his hands circling her waist when he reached her. 'You won't escape me so easily,' he murmured, blue eyes smiling.

Claire laughed up at him. 'What makes you think I want to escape? I intend to stick with you, Mr Svenson. You're going to be very rich and very famous,' she teased.

He grimaced. 'Ouch!' And then he laughed, his eyes tender. 'If I thought you meant that I'd be inclined to beat you very thoroughly indeed.'

Claire was suddenly very serious. 'I'd still love you if the film never made a penny, and you know it.'

He pulled her closer, their lower limbs tangling together. 'I don't think that you need to worry on that score. As you say *Wrecker's Bride* is going to be a success. Although how I ever managed to complete that film I shall never know. You tormented me, my darling. I never had a moment's peace. The film could have gone to hell for all I cared. In the end you were all I could think about.'

She smiled into his eyes. 'I felt just the same,' she murmured huskily. 'You know that.'

Jake gave a small rueful laugh now, as though the depth of his own feelings for her still surprised him. 'I even felt jealous this evening when I watched the film, can you believe that? When I saw Bryce kissing you I felt a tremendous urge to punch him on the nose.'

Claire hugged him tightly, her hands on his naked back, feeling the hard packed bone and muscle rippling beneath her fingers. 'I'm glad you didn't,' she said.

'Imagine the headlines tomorrow. "Director punches star on the nose at first night." It would have spoiled an otherwise perfect evening.' She paused smiling. 'I haven't thanked you yet for arranging tickets for Lynn, or for asking Mike and Joan to sit with us. I owe them a lot and I know they all enjoyed it. I thought Bryce seemed quite taken with Lynn.'

Jake's eyes gleamed wickedly. 'I don't blame him. As I've said before, she's quite a dish.'

'Jake Svenson!' Claire exclaimed.

He lowered his head and kissed her very thoroughly. 'Don't worry, my love. One woman in my life is quite enough for me to handle.' His hand moved against her spine, pulling her even closer. 'Speaking of which . . .'

Claire was so close that she could feel his heart thumping rapidly against her breast. 'I thought you were very tired,' she murmured primly.

He held her eyes with his own, passion flaring in their depths as his fingers skilfully loosened the tiny buttons at the back of her dress one by one. 'It's true, I am tired,' he muttered huskily. 'So . . . I'm going to bed.'

They had been married for six months but still Claire trembled when he touched her. 'You haven't forgotten we've an early start tomorrow. My mother will be waiting at the airport.'

'We won't miss the flight, don't worry.' He had finished loosening the buttons and lazily he pulled the soft material from her shoulders so that it fell in a pool at her feet. her slip following it slowly. Jake stared at her, his eyes lingering for a moment on her smooth white flesh, but still he didn't touch her and Claire waited, holding her breath until his lips moved possessively on to her own, banishing all desire for further conversation irrevocably from her mind.

 **ROMANCE**

Next month's romances from Mills & Boon

Each month, you can choose from a world of variety in romance with Mills & Boon. These are the new titles to look out for next month.

TEMPORARY HUSBAND Susan Alexander
LADY WITH A PAST Lillian Cheatham
PASSION'S VINE Elizabeth Graham
THE SIX-MONTH MARRIAGE Penny Jordan
ICE PRINCESS Madeleine Ker
ACT OF POSSESSION Anne Mather
A NO RISK AFFAIR Carole Mortimer
CAPTIVE OF FATE Margaret Pargeter
ALIEN VENGEANCE Sara Craven
THE WINGS OF LOVE Sally Wentworth

Buy them from your usual paperback stockist, or write to: Mills & Boon Reader Service, P.O. Box 236, Thornton Rd, Croydon, Surrey CR9 3RU, England. Readers in South Africa-write to: Mills & Boon Reader Service of Southern Africa, Private Bag X3010, Randburg, 2125.

Mills & Boon
the rose of romance

Take 4
Exciting Books
Absolutely
FREE

Love, romance, intrigue... all are captured for you by Mills & Boon's top-selling authors. By becoming a regular reader of Mills & Boon's Romances you can enjoy 6 superb new titles every month plus a whole range of special benefits: your very own personal membership card, a free monthly newsletter packed with recipes, competitions, exclusive book offers and a monthly guide to the stars, plus extra bargain offers and big cash savings.

AND an Introductory FREE GIFT for YOU.
Turn over the page for details.

As a special introduction we will send you four exciting Mills & Boon Romances Free and without obligation when you complete and return this coupon.

At the same time we will reserve a subscription to Mills & Boon Reader Service for you. Every month, you will receive 6 of the very latest novels by leading Romantic Fiction authors, delivered direct to your door. You don't pay extra for delivery — postage and packing is always completely Free. There is no obligation or commitment — you can cancel your subscription at any time.

You have nothing to lose and a whole world of romance to gain.

Just fill in and post the coupon today to **MILLS & BOON READER SERVICE, FREEPOST, P.O. BOX 236, CROYDON, SURREY CR9 9EL.**

Please Note:- READERS IN SOUTH AFRICA write to Mills & Boon, Postbag X3010, Randburg 2125, S. Africa.

FREE BOOKS CERTIFICATE

To: Mills & Boon Reader Service, FREEPOST, P.O. Box 236, Croydon, Surrey CR9 9EL.

Please send me, free and without obligation, four Mills & Boon Romances, and reserve a Reader Service Subscription for me. If I decide to subscribe I shall, from the beginning of the month following my free parcel of books, receive six new books each month for £6.60, post and packing free. If I decide not to subscribe, I shall write to you within 10 days. The free books are mine to keep in any case. I understand that I may cancel my subscription at any time simply by writing to you. I am over 18 years of age.

Please write in BLOCK CAPITALS.

Signature _____

Name _____

Address _____

_____ Post code _____

SEND NO MONEY — TAKE NO RISKS.

Please don't forget to include your Postcode.

Remember, postcodes speed delivery. Offer applies in UK only and is not valid to present subscribers. Mills & Boon reserve the right to exercise discretion in granting membership. If price changes are necessary you will be notified.

6R   *Offer expires June 30th 1985*

EP86